D1274096

LIBRARY OF JAPANESE LITERATURE

THIS SCHEMING WORLD

Portrait of Saikaku Ihara *by Kazumasa Haga*

SAIKAKU IHARA

THIS SCHEMING WORLD

translated by Masanori Takatsuka *and* David C. Stubbs

RUTLAND, VERMONT: Charles E. Tuttle Co.: TOKYO, JAPAN

Representatives

For Continental Europe:
BOXERBOOKS, INC., Zurich

For the British Isles:
PRENTICE-HALL INTERNATIONAL, INC., London

For Australasia:
PAUL FLESCH & CO., PTY. LTD., Melbourne

Published by
Charles E. Tuttle Co., Inc.
of Rutland, Vermont
and Tokyo, Japan
with editorial offices at
Suido 1-chome, 2–6, Bunkyo-ku, Tokyo

Library of Congress
Catalog Card No.
65–17850

First edition, 1965

Printed in Japan

TABLE OF CONTENTS

FOREWORD

THE LATTER half of the 17th century is a significant age in the history of Japanese literature, for it was in this age that the townspeople, who could boast of neither rank nor birth, came to hold the hegemony of literary activities.

Japanese literature had long stood far out of reach of the common people. It was either an elegant accessory or a refined pastime of the upper class. Lady Murasaki, for instance, well-known for her *Tale of Genji,* was a gentlewoman who served in the house of the great aristocrat Fujiwara Michinaga. She and her contemporaries who represented the literature of the early 11th century were either aristocrats or those who lived in a close relationship with them. Their works were appreciated with admiration by people of the upper class, but the nameless masses had nothing to do with them. Today they are esteemed by all Japanese as the valuable legacy of their ancestors, and that with good reason. Nevertheless they were, so to speak, delicate flowers cultivated in the elegant green house named aristocracy.

Why this was so is rather plain to see. A literary work cannot be conceived without regard to its readers. Of course it is true that it is the result of the writer's genius, but at the same time, because it must answer the needs of the readers of the time, it necessarily reflects its general characteristics. If the common people have little interest in literature, it is quite hopeless to expect a writer to rise from among them and write for their own sake. The Japanese common people of early times were too illiterate and too poverty-stricken to find any interest in the appreciation of literature; hence it is no wonder that they produced no literature of their own.

Then came the downfall of the aristocrats who exercised political superiority, and the rising class of warriors took their place. The new age is generally called the mediaeval age of Japan, in which the outstanding feature is the establishment of feudalism. With it the creative energies of the aristocrats ran dry and the new type of literature that succeeded the older one was more sober and grave, though less delicate and less refined, reflecting the characteristics of the warrior class that patronized it. Such was the general character of the so-called mediaeval literature of Japan that flourished from the 13th to the 16th century. Still, strictly speaking, it was not yet the literature of the common people.

The new tide swept in with the opening of the 17th century. The civil wars fought by feudal lords against one another which devastated the whole country for about two centuries were at last checked by Tokugawa Ieyasu, and the government established by him at Edo (present-day Tokyo) succeeded in maintaining nation-wide peace for the following two and a half centuries, till in 1868 it gave place to the Imperial Government. The period under the reign of the Tokugawa Government is generally called the Edo Age, so named after the seat of government.

Whereas peace deprived the warriors of their creative energy as well as of their adventurous spirit, it brought life to the townspeople. Not only the economical upper-hand, but also the cultural leadership of the country came to be held by them—a remarkable and unprecedented development in Japanese history. What is of particular significance from the viewpoint of the history of literature was that there arose a new mass of readers chiefly composed of townspeople. Their view of life was coarser and, let it be said, even vulgar, but more positive and livelier than that of the upper class. To meet their expectations a new type of literature must needs be created, which would be produced by none but a spokesman of their own. This spokesman they found in Saikaku.

Saikaku was born in 1642 in Osaka, a great center of business, and died there in 1693. His given name was Togo and his family name Hirayama. Ihara Saikaku is his pen-name. It is known to us that his wife, whom he loved dearly, died in 1675 at the age of twenty-five. In the preface to his One Thousand *Haikai* Verses, published in 1675, he relates that her death was a great shock to him, and that on the seventh day after her death he composed in her memory "one thousand *haikai* verses impromptu from morning till evening and made a clear copy of them with his own hand, for he believed he could express his love and grief the more by doing everything by himself."

Two years later, in 1677, he retired from business. It must have been partly because his wife's death left him weary of worldly pursuits. Anyway, he settled his business on one of his clerks and lived the rest of his life as freely as he pleased, travelling much and enriching his stock of information about the world, of which later he made such effective use in his works.

He had begun his literary career as a poet by composing *haikai* when he was yet a boy of fifteen. His many years' devotion to poetry established him as a figure in the world of *haikai*. But his style was revolutionary in both a good sense and a bad, for it was quite novel, lively and vigorous, and not infrequently, it might be said, indecent. It was the general opinion of his day that the composing of *haikai* should be one of the proper accomplishments of a cultured man and so its themes likewise ought to be proper. But Saikaku boldly took up such a theme as a voluptuous widow:

Oh, that cute costume of hers!
She has her hair cut short
But fire still burns within.

Or a bankrupt merchant:
He sells the house away
Where once was kept a mistress.

Or a poor fool of the gay quarter:
O that I were re-born
To share the nightly bed
With the highest courtesan.

Such a bold innovation of his could not escape bitter criticism. The orthodox *haikai* poets called him 'Holland Saikaku,' by which they meant to criticize his showy heterodoxy. Heterodox or orthodox, Saikaku's vitality could not be content with the narrow, stereotyped compass allotted to the 'elegant verbal art.'

His burning energy also found vent in the composition of as many *haikai* verses as possible in a single day. In 1684 he set the Thames on fire, so to speak, by composing as many as 23,500 verses in a single day and night.

Needless to say, a piece of literature ought to be appreciated for its quality rather than for its quantity. A single verse composed after a whole day of labor can outshine a thousand verses composed at random. In this respect it may be said that Saikaku was something of a heretic. But we must also recognize that it was this very nature of his that made him a fitting spokesman for the townspeople of his day.

As has been already pointed out, a prominent feature of the 17th century was the rise of the city dwellers as an influential class. In a word, it was the century when the bourgeoisie rose to power. Thanks to nation-wide peace, the products of even the remotest provinces were brought to market in Edo and Osaka; and the greater the volume of goods brought to market, the greater the wealth amassed by the merchants. Even the feudal lords, whose ancestors had won their territories with the sword, had to rely on these merchants for funds to run their local governments. Nominally, merchants were placed at the bottom of the social hierarchy, but actually they were kings.

The townspeople who rose to sudden eminence, having no cultural tradition of their own, were naturally coarse and vulgar in their tastes; yet in point of life and vigor they were paramount. In the days of feudalism, when too many restrictions twisted and suppressed humanity, the newly-risen bourgeoisie insisted on giving as full expression as possible to life, and Saikaku reflected perfectly their philosophy of life in his works. He could not bear literature that aspired to transcendental beauty at the sacrifice of humanity with all its merits and demerits, virtues and vices. "Man is lusty. All right. I will picture him as such. Man is greedy. Very well. I will depict him as such. Above all else I will picture the world of men and women as it actually is." Such was his attitude. After all, his genius lay more in the world of realistic fiction than in the world of verse.

In 1682 he published his first memorable work, *The Life of an Amorous Man.* It is memorable not only as his first story book but also as the first book ever written in Japan by a townsman about the life of a townsman. It is in the form of a record of the love-life of a certain Yonosuke. At the early age of seven he woos a maid who waits on him. After that he makes love to different women of some kind or other every year: to a wife, to a widow, to an inn maid, to a prostitute, to a courtesan, till he becomes sixty years old. Then, weary of the ordinary love-life of the common world, he sets sail for the Isle of Women, never to return, together with congenial spirits, who vow that it is just what the sterner sex wants and that they will not regret it even if they spend their lives exhausting their virility there.

Yonosuke, in a sense, symbolized the bourgeoisie of the time: lusty, but not hypocritical; aggressive, but not gloomy; coarse, but not affected. No wonder the book enjoyed a wide circulation. Encouraged by its success, Saikaku wrote several more works of which the central theme was love, which are now known as his amorous stories.

It may be proper to point out here that his so-called amorous stories are not to be taken as mere idle talks on love-hunters and wanton women. We may say that in them is hidden an inevitable resistance in disguise against the unnatural fetters put on humanity by feudalism.

The moral codes prescribed by Japanese feudalism laid all the restraints imaginable upon people in almost every phase of life. For instance, according to the moral code then current, a boy and a girl ought not to be seated side by side after their seventh year. Under such conditions, neither sex could be expected to develop proper manners toward the other. A boy had to become a too strict moralist, consciously evading the society of girls, if he was to be praised as an ideal boy; and a girl had to be too shy to say any words except "Yes, sire," or "Yes, madam," if she was to enjoy the name of the incarnation of female virtues. But human nature could not long be kept suppressed under such restraints. And Saikaku triumphantly proclaimed humanity free from all the restraints of feudal morals. In the light of modern times, his 'amorous stories' may seem too wanton and too erotic. Wanton and erotic they are indeed, but when we stop to consider the age in which they were written, we can see that they were a sort of declaration of humanity against the despotism of feudal morals. In a sense his 'amorous stories' are a Japanese version of Boccaccio's *Decameron.* In Yonosuke's amorous adventures, for instance, we can hear a cry of human resistance against the feudal fetters. It may appear far-fetched to argue that Saikaku consciously criticized the feudal world by the series of 'amorous stories'; none the less they were the products of a rebellious spirit against feudalism.

A born townsman, Saikaku could not overlook the queer, unnatural customs to which the warrior class was bound—especially vengeance and sodomy. Modern readers may be perplexed as to why the latter was regarded as a virtue rather than a vice. But this is no place to dwell upon it; there must have been many complicated reasons. For one thing, a young warrior could not fall in love with a girl without being criticized as being too soft. On the contrary, he was openly allowed to love a boy who was his social equal and was not yet of age. When once this relation of love between the two was announced, others had to respect it and the two had to be mutually faithful at the risk of their honor, sometimes even at the risk of their lives. This peculiar type of love then current among the warrior class attracted Saikaku's interest and in 1687 his *Mirror of Sodomy* was published.

Vengeance was another feudal virtue that attracted Saikaku's interest. If a warrior's father or elder brother or uncle was killed, he had to search all over the country to discover the murderer and take vengeance on him. Stories of successful vengeance taken after many years of hardships used to be told with admiration. But the truth was that not every case of vengeance was successful, and many of them brought misery to all concerned. So in the idealized vengeance stories current in feudal times it was inevitable that the truth was more or less distorted. Then Saikaku began to write. Born townsman, he could not compromise with the current morality and in the *Tradition of Chivalry or Records of Vengeance,* pub-

leaves with used ones. All these strugglings of men that centered around money Saikaku described with a very realistic touch.

Despite all these frantic efforts, however, not everybody could become rich. On the contrary, nine persons out of ten were destined to be failures. Especially was this true when the market was established and its shares were divided definitely, once for all, among existing merchant princes; there was then little room left for any empty-handed adventurer to aspire to wealth. Saikaku rightly wrote in *Saikaku's Last Fabrics,* published in 1694, the year after his death: "Contrary to former times, this is an age in which money begets money. Today it is the man of common ability with capital, rather than the man of rare ability with no capital, who gains profit." Indeed, in the train of a handful of shining successes there were always a host of failures groping aimlessly in the dark. And for such a realistic writer as Saikaku it was all but impossible not to pick them up in the spotlight of his works. Thus during the last stage of his career he produced a series of masterworks in which the main characters were the petty misers and failures of the world, and *This Scheming World* (Seken Munasanyo), published in 1692, is one such masterwork.

In structure *This Scheming World* is one of the most consolidated of all his works. Most of the stories are told as incidents or episodes relating to New Year's Eve, when in those days it was the custom to balance all debits and credits for the year. On this particular day of the year, the drama of life came to a climax: there were tragedies, comedies, farces and other human incidents that could not be classified into any of the regular categories of stage-plays. The players were of the nameless masses. They were not in the least aware that they were involved in a drama; they were so intent on tiding over this day of days that they were all the more pathetic for it. And

lished in 1687, he reported all varieties of vengeance—successful and unsuccessful, admirable and unreasonable, pathetic and cruel. It is notable that he dared to describe the darker aspects of vengeance in an age when it was eulogized as the very flower of chivalry.

But so far, the materials taken up by him were not good enough to show to the full his genius as a townsman writer. Only when he turned his writer's eye on the life of his fellow townsmen and started writing what are now known as 'townspeople stories' could he give full play to his unique genius. His 'townspeople stories' are quite significant in the history of Japanese literature in that they were the first literary works in which the main characters were anonymous. Yet, although the people described in these books were men of low birth and no rank, because the economical hegemony was in their hands, they were mighty giants. In *The Everlasting Storehouse of Japan,* published in 1688, Saikaku boldly declares: "Genealogy is nothing to a merchant. What is important to him is money. Even if he comes of the highest family of the land, if he is a poor tenant of a back street, he is no better than a beggar."

The newly-risen bourgeoisie knew very well what was the source of their power, why they could have an overwhelming influence in the world though lacking either family lineage to boast of or any military power to rely on. The secret of their power was money and nothing else. With money they were everything; without it they were nothing. So they clung to money desperately. How to increase it, however foul or dangerous the means might be, was the greatest concern that occupied their thoughts day and night. One of them was reluctant to walk fast, even on an emergency call to express sympathy after a fire: he feared he would work up an appetite and have to eat too much, which would mean a waste of money. Another, who was a tea-dealer, adulterated new tea

Saikaku portrayed them with so life-like a touch that even though three centuries have already passed since the days of Saikaku, it seems as if they were our contemporaries.

Modern readers, especially European and American readers, who are accustomed to reading works written strictly according to the pattern of modern short stories, may criticize Saikaku as lacking 'system.' It is true that he lacks system in the modern sense of the word. But then it must be taken into consideration that he was a writer of the 17th century, when even in Europe the pattern of short stories had not yet settled down. In a sense Saikaku's stories resemble the random chats of a worldly-wise man. Now he talks of this, then he talks of that. His talk lacks 'consistency.' Nevertheless we can picture from his description real men of flesh and blood characterized by common human weaknesses and frailties.

Had he lived longer, Saikaku might have written more works on the life of the masses, but unfortunately even as he wrote *This Scheming World* his health was already declining, and one year after its publication, in 1693, he died. He left us a short farewell poem, composed perhaps on his deathbed, the gist of which is:

"The span of human life is destined to be fifty years, which is rather too long for a man such as I. Nevertheless I was allowed to enjoy the sight of the moon of this world for two more years."

His tomb may be found in the Seiganji Temple, Osaka.

THIS SCHEMING WORLD

THE EXTRAVAGANT WIVES OF WHOLESALERS

It is the way of the world that on New Year's Eve the night is dark. Ever since the remote ages of the gods people have been clearly aware of this truth; yet they are always neglecting their business. Much to their embarrassment, they frequently find the result of their previous calculations to be all too short to tide them over the year end. This is due entirely to their ill-advised way of living.

The year end is more precious than a mint of money. It is the Great Divide between winter and spring, which none can pass over without paying a heavy toll. It is too high to be climbed by those who labor under a load of debt, which commonly results from their fond wish to provide for their children according to their means. Each separate expenditure amounts to little or nothing at the time, but the sum total for the year is quite overwhelming. The toy bow and arrow will soon be thrown into the dust bin, and even the ball of thread quickly becomes threadbare. The toy mortar used for the Dolls' Festival will be broken and the gilded sword of iris will soon fade. The drum used in the *Obon* dance will be split with too much beating, while the toy sparrows of *Hassaku,* together with the twigs from which they are suspended, will be cast aside. Furthermore, in observance of the second day of the Boar, rice cakes must be prepared, as well as dumplings for the festival of the community god. Then on December 1st coppers must be offered to exorcise the devils, and a talisman bought to neutralize the effects of ominous dreams. All these and other such things cost money, and they pile up in such abundance that no treasure boat nor single cart could hold them all.

In recent years, moreover, almost all housewives have waxed extravagant. Although not in the least short of *kimono,* they have to have another one of the very latest fashion for the New Year. It must be made as elaborately as possible: of silk that costs forty-five *momme* of silver per half *hiki;* dyed a thousand delicate tints and hues, with as many varied and intricate designs; and costing, possibly, a *ryo* of gold. In this way money is squandered on what does not really attract much attention. The *obi* must be of genuine imported satin, twelve feet long and two feet wide. Why not try wearing a girdle of two pieces of silver wound around the waist? The hair comb may cost two *ryo* of gold, but wouldn't a woman balancing three *koku* of rice on top of her head attract more attention? The petticoats must be made of crimson silk, worn in duplicate, and white *tabi* are *de rigueur.*

In olden times, even the ladies of the mightiest lords were strangers to any such luxury. If these modern wives of merchants would only pause a moment to consider, they would realize that divine retribution is bound to fall upon them. It may be excusable to some extent for a woman of means to indulge in such extravagancies. However, if her merchant husband is in debt up to his ears, with interest breeding continually, day and night, rain or shine, it is not a burden to be shrugged off lightly. Rather should the wife be more prudent, and be thoroughly ashamed of herself for indulging in such luxuries. Is it barely possible that she is laying in a supply of expensive stuff against the day when her husband, who may be even now teetering on the brink of bankruptcy, will be completely ruined? After all, women's possessions are exempt from attachment: maybe the wife means to pawn the goods to raise money. However, generally speaking, a woman is so shallow pated that even on the very eve of her husband's bankruptcy she will fare forth in a sedan chair, attended by two men each bearing a lantern, a quite superfluous accessory in the moonlight. Her actions are as vain and futile as wearing rich brocade in the dark, or as silly as pouring cold water into hot after you've taken the trouble to boil it.

From his place of enshrinement within the household altar, the deceased father witnesses this procession of follies. Though sorely vexed, it's useless to admonish his son and heir, the current master of the household, for the two are living in entirely different worlds. Yet to himself he says: "My son's business is basically unsound. He buys ten *kan* worth of goods and sells them for eight *kan*. This kind of so-called 'business management' results in nothing but the decrease of capital. By the end of the year it's inevitable that an auction notice will be posted on his door. It will announce that this house of ninety-foot frontage, including three strong rooms, will be sold at auction to the highest bidder, together with all its furniture and mats (both high-and middle-class) numbering two hundred and forty in all, along with an inter-coastal vessel and a five-passenger pleasure craft, plus a small rowboat, the said auction to be held on the nineteenth day of January next, at the town hall."

Thus will all the son's property fall into the hands of others, all of which the father foresees with deep regret. He likewise discerns, beyond a shadow of a doubt, that the paraphernalia used in the Buddhist religious services will also pass into other hands. Therefore he appears to his son in a dream with a timely warning:

"That trio of bronze treasures is among our dearest family heirlooms," he says, "much too precious to pass into the hands of outsiders. I'll have to have them wrapped up in a lotus leaf, to take back with me to Paradise this July when you light the *Obon* Fire to speed my parting spirit. After all, the inherited business of this house won't survive the year end. When you bought that considerable parcel of rice land in Tamba Province, my boy, you probably realized that yourself, didn't you, thinking to provide a place of retreat? Actually, however, that transaction was nothing but a piece of indiscretion. If you think you're so smart, just remember that the man who finances you is no less clever. Nothing will escape his scrutiny, and no alternative remains for you: lock, stock, and barrel—everything will pass into the hands of strangers. Instead of playing the fool—and that to no purpose—why don't you apply yourself to business? Even though I'm dead, my son, I have appeared to you in this dream because I love you." Thus spoke the deceased father.

The dream passed, the morning of December 29th dawned, and the young merchant awoke, shaking with laughter in his bed. "Dear, O dear!" he exclaimed. "To see the old gentleman in a dream just at this busy year end! How perfectly shocking to discover that my dead father is still so grasping that even in the other world he wants me to donate that trio of treasures to the temple."

But even as he spoke these disparaging words on his deceased father the creditors came pouring in, one after another. How was he to meet the situation?

Well, in recent days, merchants short of money have originated the idea of a so-called bill of exchange, or draft. Whenever they can spare the cash, they deposit it with a bill broker without interest, on condition that when the need arises he will pay it out for them. A rather clever device it is, convenient alike to both creditor and borrower. Our young merchant likewise, making use of this new system, had deposited twenty-five *kan* of silver toward the end of November with a trusted broker. When the time for the general settlement of debts arrived at the year end, he handed one draft to the rice dealer, another to the draper, a third to the bean-paste dealer, a fourth to the fishmonger—indeed, to each and every creditor who came along he made out a draft, saying it would be cashed by his broker. He even paid his dues to the Kannon Worship Society with a draft, as well as his bills to the bawdyhouse.

Then, proclaiming that all had been attended to, he pushed off for Sumiyoshi Shrine, to spend the last night of the old year in calm, unruffled prayer. Yet the waves in his bosom never ceased to roll. Perhaps the god of Sumiyoshi felt somewhat uneasy at accepting gifts from such a fellow.

Now whereas the drafts he had drawn on the broker totaled eighty *kan* of silver, only twenty-five *kan* was on deposit. Hence the broker announced that since there were too many bills to be cleared, none would be cashed until all the other accounts had been duly settled. While the broker was inquiring more carefully into the matter, the drafts were wafted about from one creditor to another, until at last the confusion was so confounded that none could tell who had which draft. The end result was that they were forced to speed the parting old year with dishonored bills on hand.

Then came the dawn! The dawn of a truly auspicious New Year.

PAWNING AN OLD HALBERD SHEATH

A SOLAR eclipse occurred on New Year's Day sixty-nine years ago, and when again on the selfsame day in the fifth year of Genroku another occurred, people witnessed a most uncommon dawn of the New Year. As for the calendar, in the fourth year of the reign of Empress Jito, there was inaugurated the Giho Calendar, which was based upon the eclipses of the sun and moon. Ever since then the people have trusted the calendar.

Now, the days moved quickly by, one after another, from the top of the calendar to the bottom, until at last they reached the nethermost rung. It is then that people become so busily occupied that not a sound can be heard —not a tune—not even a hum. In the poorer quarters particularly they find it necessary to quarrel, to wash, and to repair the foundations of the walls all at the same time. The result is that they lack time to prepare for the New Year. Not one piece of rice cake, nor even a dried sardine, do they have. Poor and miserable indeed is their life when compared with that of the rich. How in the world do they manage to tide over the year end, these people who are crowded into half a dozen or more narrow sections of a single tenement-house?

Because each of them has something or other to pawn, they show no signs of anxiety. With the one exception of rent, which is paid at the end of each month, they are accustomed every day of their lives to buy for cash whatever necessities of life they may need, such as rice, bean paste, firewood, vinegar, soy sauce, salt, oil, and the like; for nobody will sell them anything on credit. So when the end of the month comes, no creditor will slip up on them unannounced with his account book open, nor is there anyone for them to be afraid of, or anyone to whom they must apologize for unpaid bills. In their case, the saying of the old sage indeed holds true: "Pleasure lies in poverty."

People who refuse to pay their debts are no better than daylight burglars in disguise. In brief, because they make only a very rough estimate for the year, not figuring their income and outgo month by month, most people find their income insufficient to make both ends meet. But in the case of people who live from hand to mouth things are different. Can they improve their lot by taking pains to enter their expenditures in an account book? Why, even on the very eve of the New Year their daily life is not a bit different from what it is the other days of the year. How is it possible in such circumstances for them to celebrate the New Year? Their only expectation, poor chaps, lies in their pawning whatever they may happen to have at hand.

For example, one of them will pawn an old umbrella, a cotton gin and a teakettle, which enables him to have one *momme* of silver with which to tide over the season. As for the chap who lives next door to him, the pawnable articles he finds are his wife's everyday *obi* (she will make paper string do), his cotton hood, a set of picnic lunch boxes with the top lid missing, a weaving frame 300 threads wide, a five-*go* and a one-*go* measure, five porcelain dishes manufactured in Minato, and a hanging Buddhist altar with assorted service attachments—a grand total of twenty-three items in all, for which he receives the magnificent sum of one *momme* and six in silver to get through the year end.

The neighbor living to the east of him is a dancing beggar, who during the New Year season is accustomed to switch to the Daikoku dance. Since an appropriate mask costing five *mon* and a papier-mâché mallet will suffice for the season, unnecessary are his headgear, his dancing *kimono,* and his *hakama.* So these he will pawn for two *momme* and seven, and thus pass the year end in tranquillity.

Next door to him lives a trouble-making *ronin* who wears only paper clothes, for he has long since sold off his weapons and harness to buy food. Hitherto he has managed to scrape out a bare living by making toy fishing tackle, using the hairs from horses' tails. But as these are now passé, he is quite reduced to want and is at a complete loss as to how to tide over the year end. Finally, in desperation he sends his wife to the pawnbroker's with their old halberd sheath. No sooner has the pawnbroker picked it up, however, than he throws it back at the woman, remarking that it is worthless. In an instant her countenance changes and in a fit of rage she screams, "Why do you throw my precious possession about? If you won't take it in pledge, just say so! 'Worthless,' you say? Such abusive words cannot be ignored. This is the sheath of the very halberd my dead father used when he so valiantly distinguished himself at the time of Ishida's revolt. Having no son, he gave it to me, and when in better days I was married, it sheathed the very halberd in my wedding procession. To disparage it is to abuse the memory of my brave father who is now in heaven. I'm only a woman, I know, but I'm ready this very instant to die if need be. Now I'll fight!" So saying she grabs the pawnbroker around the waist with all her might, at the same time bursting into tears. Overwhelmed with embarrassment, the pawnbroker apologizes as profusely as possible, but the angry woman is not to be so easily appeased.

Meantime the neighbors have come thronging into the shop, and one of them whispers into the pawnbroker's ear that he'd better settle the matter before word reaches the ears of her husband, for he is a notorious blackmailer. So after much ado, he manages to settle the trouble by offering her three hundred *mon* in copper, plus three *sho* of rice. Alas, to what depths has she sunk. This raging woman was once the beloved daughter of a warrior whose annual stipend was twelve hundred *koku* of rice. Accustomed to living at ease in her better days, it is only her present poverty that has driven her into such unconscionable blackmailing. Recollecting her illustrious past, she must have been filled with a sense of shame. From a single example such as this one, it is apparent that it just won't do for anyone to die poor!

Well, anyway, the matter now being settled, she receives the three hundred copper *mon* and the three *sho* of rice. But unhulled rice, she complains, will be useless on the morrow. "Oh, fortunately, Ma'am," replies the pawnbroker, "I happen to have a mortar right here. You are welcome to use it to hull the rice." Could this incident be cited as a good illustration of the saying, "A touch will cost you three hundred *mon*"?

Next door to the *ronin* lives a woman of thirty-seven or thirty-eight years, all alone, for she has no relatives, not even a son to depend on. Her husband, she says, died several years ago; so she had her hair cut short and has worn plain clothes ever since. Yet she still cares for her personal appearance as much as ever, and she retains a definite though unostentatious air of elegance about her. She usually spends her days spinning hempen thread, just to pass the time away. Already by early December she has completed her preparations for the New Year: her stock of firewood will last until February or March; on the fish hanger hang a medium-sized yellowtail, five small porgies, and two codfish; and everything—from lacquered chopsticks and Kii lacquerware down to the very lids of the pots—all is brand new. She makes a year-end present of a salt mackerel to her landlord, a pair of silk-strapped *geta* to his daughter, and a pair of *tabi* to his wife; while to each of her fellow tenants she presents a rice cake and a bundle of burdock. Thus she passes the year end by discharging every social obligation. How she makes a living is her own well-guarded secret.

Next door to her live a couple of women, the younger one of whom has ears, eyes, and a nose that are not in the least bit different from those of other girls. Yet to her great sorrow she is yet unmarried. Whenever she views herself in her mirror, however, she is compelled to realize anew why no one ever takes a second look at her. The other woman, who is older, once served as a maid in an inn on the Tokaido highway, near the town of Seki. While working there she mistreated the young men making secret pilgrimages to the shrine at Ise, and would pilfer their scanty supply of rice. Divine retribution overtook her while yet in this world, however, and she is now a poor mendicant nun. Pretending to be pious, she chants sutras devoid of devotion. A nun in form, she is but an ogre in spirit, a veritable wolf in sheep's clothing. So impious is she that it never even occurs to her that she ought to abstain from eating meat. Yet for the past fourteen or fifteen years she has, by the mercy of the Buddha, managed to eke out a living, only because of her black clerical robe made of hemp. For as the saying goes, "Even a sardine's head will shine if believed in." Each morning as she walks about the streets begging rice she receives alms from an average of two houses per street, which means that to gather even a single *go* of rice she must visit as many as twenty houses. She cannot hope to garner five *go* of rice until she has walked through at least fifty streets. It surely takes a healthy person to be a mendicant nun!

Unfortunately, during the previous summer, she suffered a sunstroke, which necessitated her pawning the clerical robe for one *momme* and eight. Since then, as she has been unable to redeem the robe by any means, she has lost her means of livelihood. Of course we should not jump to the conclusion that people have become any less generous in almsgiving for the sake of their souls in the afterlife. Yet now that she is without the clerical robe, she cannot expect to collect even two *go* of rice a day; whereas formerly when wearing it she usually received five *go*. "December priest and priestess" runs the well-known saying. Yes, especially in December when people are so busy that they forget even the services in memory of their departed parents, it is no wonder that they do not care to give alms to a mendicant nun. So, with only eight *mon* in hand, she must somehow tide over the year end.

Surely no one is in a better position to understand the misery in this world than is the cheap pawnbroker who keeps shop among the poverty-stricken in the slums. Indeed, even to the eyes of the casual bystander it is obvious that the year end is replete with things both sad and pitiable.

WHEN ISE LOBSTERS WERE AS SCARCE AS CRIMSON LEAVES IN SPRINGTIME

DURING the New Year season it is customary to set out *Horai* decorations. But without Ise lobsters to top them, the celebration of the New Year seems incomplete. It occasionally happens, however, that the price of the lobsters rises so high that a poor man or a penny pincher has to celebrate the New Year without any.

A few years ago, when the supply of bitter oranges was so short that a single orange cost four or five *bu*, many people substituted bergamot oranges, which were all right because they closely resemble bitter oranges in shape and color. But in the case of Ise lobsters, to use a prawn as a substitute would be no more fitting than to wear borrowed clothes.

The man who lives in a lofty mansion and has a reputation to uphold often finds that the winds of the world blow against his house so much harder that ordinary straw matting cannot protect his walls from the rain. It is only natural for him to cover them with wainscoting painted with persimmon tannin mixed with lamp black. For him this is no luxury, but a necessity. It's really no pleasure at all unless you eat, and dress, and live in a house in a style that accords with your means.

I might add, incidentally, that very few men have ever succeeded, whatever their business, when they altered the inherited way of managing it and ventured on some new enterprise. It is better to take the advice of the old veterans. No matter how talented a young man may be, it often happens that in the end his advance calculations are completely frustrated.

Now in Osaka the year-end scene resembles nothing so much as a treasure mart. People there are always complaining aloud that business has been bad. Actually, however, for the past sixty years they have never had to throw anything away because it hasn't been sold. Even millstones, which last a lifetime and can even be passed on down to posterity, are sold so regularly every day, year in and year out, that there's danger the very hills from which they are quarried will eventually disappear. If this be true of millstones, it seems only natural that such seasonal things as the offerings for the *Obon* Festival in July, the toy helmets used in the Boys' Festival in May, and the things used in celebration of the New Year—all of which last but a few days—should be prepared anew each year when the proper season rolls around. Gift fans presented by temples to their parishioners are thrown away without ever having been unwrapped. No one seems even to be conscious of such a wasteful way of living. Indeed, as free spenders the citizens of Osaka are second only to the people of Edo.

Now this particular year of which I write it happened that everyone in the city, vowing that his New Year decorations would be incomplete without an Ise lobster, determined to buy one even if it cost a thousand *kan*. The result was that by December 27th or 28th the supply of Ise lobsters was so exhausted that in every fishmonger's shop in Osaka they were as scarce as imported articles. And by New Year's Eve not even a whiff of one was to be detected, high or low; all along the shore and in every fisherman's hut you could hear the plaintive voices of buyers asking if there were any Ise lobsters for sale.

At a fishmonger's shop called the Era, located in the middle of Bingo Street in Osaka, there happened to be just one Ise lobster left. The bidding for it began at one and a half *momme* and finally rose to four *momme* and eight. Even at that exhorbitant price, however, the fishmonger refused to part with it, claiming that its like could not be found anywhere else.

Since it was far beyond the authority of a mere servant to buy it at such an inflated price on his own responsibility, he returned home hastily to his master and explained the situation. Whereupon the master frowned and said: "Never in my life have I bought anything that was too expensive. I make it a rule to buy firewood in June, cotton in August, rice before the *sake*-brewing season starts, and hemp just after the *Bon* season. In brief, my principle is to buy for cash when the price is cheapest. The only exception (and one which I have ever since remembered with regret) was made when my father died: I bought an expensive coffin at the price quoted by the cooper. There is no reason in the world why, willy-nilly, we should have to greet the New Year with an Ise lobster installed in our house. I'll make up for its absence this year by buying two of them next year when the price comes down to only three *mon* apiece. I don't mind in the least if due to the absence of an Ise lobster the New Year god is reluctant to visit my house. No, not in the least! I wouldn't buy one if the price were reduced to four *momme*—no, not even if it were only four *bu!*"

Despite the master's wry face, his wife and son both thought it just wouldn't do at all to be without an Ise lobster. They could bear up under the thought of losing face publicly, but when the daughter's husband would make his first New Year's call on his wife's parents and see no Ise lobster crowning the New Year decorations—that scene was simply unthinkable. They must have one at any cost. Back went the servant posthaste, but he was too late, for another servant of a wholesaler from Imabashi had already bought the Ise lobster. The price quoted had been five *momme* and eight, but since it was appropriate to usher in the New Year with round figures, an even five hundred *mon* had been paid for it. The last lobster having been sold, then, all further forays of the servant to hunt lobsters were fruitless; so he had to return home, empty-handed, a sadder but wiser man, more conscious than ever of the great size of Osaka, and confess all to his master and mistress.

The mistress looked sorrowful, but the master laughed and said: "I feel uneasy about any wholesaler who would buy a lobster at so fancy a price. He's bound to go bankrupt before long. His financial backer, unaware of his real circumstances, is sure to have a nightmare over the holiday season. If a lobster is indispensable for the decoration, I have an idea for making one that will keep much longer than a live one." So saying, he commissioned an artisan to fashion a lobster of crimson silk, which cost him only two and a half *momme*. "Look," he pointed out, "it will be useful as a toy for the baby even after the season is all over. That's the way a wise man does things. A thing that would have cost you four *momme* and eight has been provided for two and a half *momme*. And what's more, it can be used over and over again."

Since there was no gainsaying the master's proud boast, everyone was forced to listen to him and acknowledge the rare wisdom of one who could attain to such wealth as he possessed.

While all this was going on, the master's old mother, who was ninety-two years of age, but was still able to see well and to walk as well as ever, entered the room from her quarters in the annex. "I hear that you're making a lot of fuss over the price of a lobster," she remarked. "It was foolish of you not to have bought one ahead of time. With such negligence how in the world can you expect to keep this shop? You should remember that always just before the New Year season lobsters are expensive, not only because the Grand Shrine at Ise and all its subordinate shrines, including the temporary offices where the underling priests are sent, need lobsters, but also because at this season there are millions of them in demand by every household in every town and countryside that holds a festival to the gods—and truly this is a land of the gods! The lobsters brought into Kyoto and Osaka each year are those left over, after the gods have had their fill. Now it just happens that I took all this into consideration and about the middle of the month I bought two lobsters as fresh and natural as they came out of the sea. Perfect specimens: even their feelers have never been joined together. And the price I paid for them? Just four *mon* apiece, you see."

Admiring applause greeted the old mother's announcement, but some ventured to criticize her extravagance in buying two lobsters when really one would have done. "I don't spend my money to no purpose," she retorted. "There's a man who every year presents me with five bundles of burdock—three, if the burdock is thick—and I must give him in return something of like value. My plan was to give him a lobster that cost me four *mon* in return for the burdock which ought to be worth about one *momme*. It's pretty lucky for you that he hasn't come yet with his usual year-end present. I tell you what I'll do: I'll let you have one of my lobsters, but remember that business is business even between mother and son. If you really want the lobster, then you'll have to send somebody to me with five bundles of burdock. I don't care who gets the lobster, just so long as I get my burdock in exchange for it. And anyway, you can't celebrate the New Year without it. Not that I'm speaking from any selfish motive, understand. It's just that in giving and receiving presents on the five annual festival days you have to make rather careful calculations of what you receive. In return, you have to give things which, while seeming to be equal in value, actually allow you a slight margin of profit.

"For example, every year the Ise priests present our

family with a good-luck charm, a set of dried bonito, a box of face powder, a folding calendar, and five bundles of green laver. If you make a close calculation of their value it comes to about two *momme* and eight. Now from our house we always used to offer three *momme*, which meant that the difference of two odd *bu* represented a profit for the Grand Shrine of Ise. For thirty years this was our practice, but since you've become master of this house, each year you have offered one piece of silver. That's unconscionably too much!—even if it is an act of devotion. Why, even the shrine gods themselves would frown with disapproval upon anyone who spent money without due consideration. Take for example that offertory coin called a Pigeon's Eye. Contrary to what most people think, one *kan* of these round lead coins with a hole in the middle is actually worth only six hundred *mon*. From this it is quite apparent that the gods themselves are concerned that pilgrimages be made with due economy."

No matter how we look at it, this whole world is filled with greed. Of all the hundred and twenty subordinate shrines of Ise, the two which enjoy the richest offerings are those of Ebisu and Daikoku. Taga is the god of long life, Sumiyoshi the guardian of boatmen, and Izumo the deity of go-betweens. Kagami, of course, makes girls look pretty; while Sanno is the chief of twenty-one minor deities. Inari is the god who sees to it that property does not pass out of the family. Or at least so claim the shrine "sparrows," those mercantile henchmen of the various gods, who chirp their praises to visitors to their shrines. But never mind. Because they are all gods who possess some pleasing attribute, people make offerings to them. But all about the shrines of the other gods there hangs a pall of solemn loneliness. In view of the fact that we are living in an age when even the gods cannot earn money without exerting themselves, it follows as a matter of course that human beings ought never to be caught off guard.

It is a custom of the priests at the Grand Shrine at Ise to send out New Year's greetings to their devoted patrons all over the land. Since this calls for the writing of a large number of letters, skilled calligraphers who are paid one *mon* per letter are employed to write them. From one New Year's Day to the next they are busy writing the same letters over and over again, but they never earn more than about two hundred *mon* a day. Why do they engage in such an occupation? For the sake of the everlasting prosperity which springs from the divine virtue, for the peace of the people, for the sake of devotion, and last but not least, to earn a livelihood.

THE MOUSE MESSENGER

THERE once lived a man whose invariable practice it was to clean house every thirteenth of December. From the family temple he would receive twelve bushed bamboo poles. He preferred the number twelve because it was a lucky one, symbolizing the months of the year. Anything connected with such an auspicious occasion as the year end has to be related to a lucky number. After using them to clean up around the house, he would use the stocks of the poles to reinforce his thatched roof. As for the twigs, he would affix them to a broom head, thus making certain that no part of the lucky bamboo should be disposed of as useless. Such was the unvarying habit of this parsimonious fellow.

But it happened one year that he was so busy on the thirteenth of December that he postponed his house cleaning until New Year's Eve, at which time he also prepared a hot bath, for the first and the last time of the year. It was in connection with this that he customarily utilized the waste leaves of the May *chimaki,* the lotus leaves left from the *Bon* season, and other miscellaneous odds and ends that he'd saved up to use as fuel to heat the bath. In his opinion there was no need to be particular about the type of fuel consumed, just so long as it heated the bath water. Not wishing to be wasteful in the least, he was extremely careful about even the minutest matters.

His aged mother lived in the cottage annex, built to the rear of his house, and as might well be expected of the woman who had given birth to such a skinflint as he, she was as stingy as stingy could be. As she, too, was about to add fuel to the bath firebox by throwing in one odd lacquered *geta* she was reminded of her past. "The pair of *geta* of which this was the fellow," she sighed audibly, "were first brought to this house in my bridal chest when I was married at the age of eighteen. Ever since then I have worn them every day, in rain or snow. Though the undersupports have worn out several times, they've stayed in good condition all these fifty-three years. I had hoped they would last me until I died, but to my great regret one of them was carried off by a stray dog the other day. This single one isn't much good by itself, so I've got to burn it for fuel."

So complaining time and again, she tossed the lone *geta* into the firebox. But this very action brought painful memories of still another regrettable incident. So again she began complaining and bewailing the fact that "time flies like an arrow." "The first anniversary will come around tomorrow," she moaned, "to make me sad all over again."

A physician who lived in her neighborhood happened to be taking his bath. "Stop your grieving," he called out to her. "The year end is an auspicious occasion. Incidentally, who was it that died a year ago for whom you will be observing an anniversary?" he inquired.

"I'm just a foolish old woman," she answered, "but when human beings die I don't grieve so much for them, because everybody must die sooner or later. What really makes me sad is this: last New Year's Day my sister from Sakai paid me a New Year's call and brought me a present of some money. I was so happy that I at once placed it on the shelf dedicated to the god of the New Year. But that same night it was stolen. No outsider could have taken it. When all my prayers, first to this god and then to that, went unanswered, I asked a *yamabushi* (mountain monk) to perform a divination for me. He said that if the sacred paper on the altar shook and the sacred light gradually died out, it would signify that the missing money would be restored within seven days. Sure enough, the paper did begin to shake and the light went out. So deeply was I moved by this divine manifestation, which seemed to me proof that the world was not yet hopelessly degenerate, that I gave the *yamabushi* all of a hundred and twenty *mon*. After that I waited for seven days, but the money never turned up.

"I was telling this to another man, and he said that what I had done was just like throwing good money after bad. Nowadays, he told me, 'there are so-called *yamabushi* who are fakes. For instance, they'll fix up various contrivances under the altar by means of which they can make paper dolls dance the Tosa dance. This is not at all new,' he continued, 'but was originally performed by a magician by the name of Matsuda. People nowadays are highly sophisticated, but for that very reason they sooner fall into the simplest of traps. The shaking of the sacred paper,' he went on, 'is caused by loaches concealed in a pot on the stand to which the paper is attached. The fake *yamabushi* rubs his rosary and chants an incantation, all the while wildly beating on the altar with a sacred stick. This commotion so frightens the loaches that they start jumping up and down. When in motion they touch the sacred paper and make it shake, striking awe into those who are not in on the trick. As for the light, in the stand there's fixed a device resembling an hourglass which cuts off the supply of oil and makes the light go out.'

"When I heard this story from the man," lamented the old woman, "I realized at once that I had suffered loss upon loss. Never in my life until then had I lost even one *mon*. But now on this very New Year's Eve I find that my calculations have gone all awry. Since the money's still missing, everything looks dark for me, and I must face the New Year with a troubled spirit." So saying, the old woman burst into such a fit of unrestrained crying that it embarrassed the servants and the entire family. Furthermore, they were vexed at her suspecting them of theft, and they swore in the names of various gods that they were entirely innocent.

Meantime the house cleaning was almost done, but just as the servants reached the attic, one of them spied something wrapped up in Sugihara paper. It was the very money for which the old woman had been searching for so long a time. "You see?" they said to her. "What was never stolen is bound to turn up sooner or later. My! What a mischievous mouse that was!" But she was not to be mollified. Pounding the mats with her fists she cried out that never in her born days had she seen a mouse, or even heard of one, that could carry something that far. "I think it must have been a two-legged rat," she insisted, "so I'll still have to keep a sharp watch."

Just at this point the physician, who had just finished his bath, came over and said, "It seems to me that there are some ancient precedents that apply here. For example, on New Year's Eve in the first year of Taika, in the reign of the 37th Emperor, Kotoku, the Imperial Residence was removed from Okamoto in Yamato to Nagara-Toyosaki in Naniwa. At the same time the mice of Yamato also moved. Now the thing that is so fascinating is that they carried along with them all their household effects: old cotton to line their holes with, paper to shelter them from the eyes of hawks, amulet cases to keep off the cats, pointed pickets to block the weasel's way, sticks to prop open mousetraps, boards to extinguish lights with, levers to use when hooking dried bonito, desiccated sea-ears to use at weddings, heads of dried sardines, and bags of broken rice for use on pilgrimages to Kumano—all these they carried along in their mouths, throughout the entire two days' journey. How simple then it must have been for this mouse to carry your money so short a distance as that between the cottage annex and the main house!" In such fashion the good physician undertook to pacify her, but his learned quotations from ancient times were all to no avail. She still insisted that she would not be convinced by any mere speech, no matter how clever, but must see some concrete evidence with her own eyes.

Everyone was perplexed as to what to do, but finally they remembered that a certain Tobei had a mouse that had been trained by Nagasaki Mizuemon to perform tricks. So they sent for him, and when he arrived they asked the old woman to watch the mouse perform its various tricks. When Tobei told the mouse that a boy wanted a love letter delivered for him, it picked up a sealed envelope in its mouth, looked all around, and then placed it in the *kimono* sleeve of a girl who happened to be standing by. Next Tobei threw it a one-*mon* coin, ordering it to go buy a rice cake. At once it found a rice cake and returned with it, leaving the coin in its place.

"Now you are convinced, aren't you?" they asked the old woman.

"Well," she replied, "now that I have seen an actual demonstration, I don't deny that a mouse could have carried off my money. But my suspicions are not completely allayed. It's most unfortunate that the master let such a thieving mouse stay in his house. Since it was due to his carelessness that my money was laid away for a whole year serving no useful purpose, he ought at least to pay me interest for the period of time it was missing."

So on New Year's Eve under such a pretext as this she extorted from her parsimonious son interest at the rate of fifteen per cent. Then muttering that now she was in a proper mood to celebrate the arrival of the New Year, she made her way back to her lonely bed.

THE ONE-*MOMME* CLUB

WHEN a man becomes rich, people always say he's lucky. But this is merely a conventional expression, for in reality he becomes rich and his household thrives solely on account of his own ability and foresight. Even Ebisu, the god of wealth, is unable at will to exercise power over riches.

But be that as it may, our wealthy merchants, for whom the discussion of a pending loan to a feudal lord is a far more engaging pastime than carousing or any other form of merrymaking, have recently organized themselves into the Daikoku Club. Shunning a rendezvous in the red-light district, they gather in the guest room of the Buddhist temple in Shimotera, Ikutama. There they meet every month to discuss the financial condition of each individual applicant for a loan. Though they are all well along in years, they take pleasure only in ever-increasing interest and in mounting capital, utterly heedless of the life to come. Although it's quite true that there's nothing more desirable than plenty of money, the proper way for a man to get along in the world should be this: in his youth until the age of twenty-five to be ever alert, in his manly prime up to thirty-five to earn a lot of money, in the prime of discretion in his fifties to pile up his fortune, and at last in his sixties—the year before his sixty-first birthday—to turn over all his business to his eldest son. Thereafter it is proper for him to retire from active affairs and devote the remainder of his days to visiting temples for the sake of his soul.

These wealthy merchants of the Daikoku Club, however, who have already arrived at an age when it is eminently respectable to spend their days visiting temples, continue to live in the midst of an avaricious world, completely oblivious to the way of the Buddha. Although every single one of them is worth two thousand *kan* or more, when he dies, all his property will remain in this world. He couldn't take anything along with him—except a shroud—if he possessed ten thousand *kan.*

In recent days, another less wealthy group—twenty-eight members in all—who have through their own efforts amassed only from two or three to five hundred *kan,* have formed themselves into the One-Momme Club. They have no regular meeting place, but wherever they gather for a meal they never order a dish that costs more than one *momme.* (Hence the name of the club.) No *sake* is served with the food, though all of them are not teetotalers. How suffocatingly prudent it is to be so careful of money spent even for recreation!

From morning till night the men talk of nothing but money. Principally they scrutinize this merchant or that, to decide whether or not it is safe to make him a loan. They have accumulated their fortunes by loaning money and battening on the interest; indeed, there's no business more profitable than money lending. Nowadays, however, there are a goodly number of merchants who, while putting up a prosperous front, are actually hard pressed. It frequently happens that when such merchants have obtained a loan and go bankrupt, they inflict painful and unanticipated losses upon their financial backers. In spite of this, it would never do for these moneyed men to display an overweening distrust of them by outright refusal to grant them loans. "Since this is the situation," they say to each other, "let's look into the financial condition of each applicant for a loan as best we can, and then pool our information before deciding to whom we will make loans. And since all of us have agreed to this procedure, let's not try to outwit each other."

"Now then, just for our information," suggests one of the club members, "let's first of all make a list of all those who regularly borrow money from us." To which several reply, "That's a very good idea!"

"First of all," suggests another, "let's consider Mr. So-and-so, that merchant in Kitahama. His property *in toto* is probably worth about seven hundred *kan*."

"Oh, no!" protests another. "That's wide of the mark. I happen to know that he has debts outstanding that total eight hundred and fifty *kan*."

Whereupon the entire company, being astonished that there exists such a wide discrepancy between the two opinions expressed, call for a closer inspection and ask for further details.

"The reason I believe him to be rich," volunteers one of the company, "is this: a year ago last November his daughter married a merchant who lives in Sakai. Their bridal train stretched all the way from Imamiya to Fuji-no-maru's Pharmacy in Nagamachi Street. And that's not all. That long procession was followed by five chests, carried by tall men of equal height and suspended from green bamboo poles, each chest containing ten *kan* of silver. It looked just like a shrine festival procession. This merchant has several sons in addition to the daughter. If he wasn't rich, I figured, he couldn't have given her a dowry of fifty *kan*. So just last March I urged him to accept a loan from me of twenty *kan,* which he did with seeming reluctance."

Up spoke one of the other members of the One-Momme Club: "That's too bad! I'm afraid that twenty *kan* of yours will come back to you diminished to exactly one *kan* and six hundred *mon*."

Hearing him, the original speaker turned pale, paused with his chopsticks midway to his mouth, and became so agitated that he left off sipping his fish and vegetable soup. "How sad the news I hear today!" he cried, and his tears began to flow even before he had heard the substantiating details. "Please," he begged, "tell me all all about it!"

"Well," replied the other man, "the father of that bridegroom is so badly in need of funds that he's willing to pay the same high interest rates that play producers have to pay. Do you know of any other business beside the theater that can afford to pay such exorbitant interest rates and remain solvent? As for those ten-*kan* chests of silver you saw in the bridal procession, you could have them duplicated—with metal fittings, too—for about three and a half *momme* apiece. The five chests probably cost him no more than seventeen and a half *momme*. There were probably stones, or broken tile, inside, or practically any old thing that weighs enough. Surely there's nothing worse than human depravity! My best guess is that those five money chests represented an effort on the part of the two households to deceive the world as to their true financial condition. As for me, even if I'd opened them up and found real silver inside I'd still not have believed it. Two hundred pieces of silver is just too much of a dowry for the daughter of a merchant who has no more money than he has. Not taking into account the value of the rest of the trousseau, I'd say that a dowry of about five *kan* would be plenty for his daughter. What do you think of my estimate? It might be best to let him have a loan of say two *kan* at first for a year or two, as a kind of test case. If the loan proves a safe one, then we may offer to lend him up to four or five *kan* for a period of some five or six years. I think that until he has proved himself to be thoroughly reliable, a loan of twenty *kan* is much too risky."

The whole company expressed their approval of his judgment. However, the man who had already made the loan of twenty *kan,* now being completely convinced by the arguments of the more experienced member of the company, became so dejected that he could hardly rise to his feet when the meeting was over. Sighing, he said: "In all my life I've never before misjudged the financial status of any man, but this time I must admit that I've been indiscreet." How, he inquired tearfully, might he recover his loan?

"There is only one safe and sure way to get your money back," replied the worldly-wise man who had just delivered the contrary judgment. "And even if you wracked your wits for a thousand days and nights, you could think of no other. For a present of one *hiki* of extra fine pongee I'll tell you how you can do it," he offered.

"That's very kind of you. I'll certainly accept that offer," answered the downcast one whose judgment had been found faulty. "Furthermore, to show my gratitude, I'll add padding to the pongee. Please reveal the secret to me."

"First of all," replied the man of wisdom, "you must cultivate his acquaintance more closely. Fortunately, the Temma Boat Festival is not far off. On the 25th send your wife to view it from the beach stands. At that time let her fall into casual conversation with the wife of your merchant debtor about various household matters and spend an enjoyable day with her. Later, of course, for courtesy's sake her sons will be introduced to your wife. When they are, she must praise the second son for his handsomeness, saying something like this:

" 'Oh, what intelligent-looking eyes your son has—so bright and sparkling! Forgive my rudeness, but I just can't help saying that this son of yours is like a peacock born to a kite. No wonder he's called an Adonis. I don't mean to over persuade you, but I'd love to have him for a son-in-law, and I say it in sober seriousness. My own daughter, though her mother obviously is a very plain person, has ordinary good looks. Besides, since she's the only child, her father has always said he'd give her a dowry of fifty *kan* when she marries. Besides, there's that three hundred and fifty *ryo* that I have for my private use. And then that corner house at Nagabori—it must be worth at least twenty-five *kan*. And I almost forgot to mention those sixty-five sets of *kimono*, still in as brand-new condition as the day they were made. She's the only one who can possibly inherit them in the future. How I wish this handsome son of yours could be her husband!'

"While your wife is speaking in this fashion she should be gazing longingly all the while at the son. So much for the first step. Now from time to time after that you should send presents of something or other to the merchant. Since he'll pay you back with things of approximately the same value, fear no loss in that quarter. Then at the proper moment you should have the son brought into your office to help your clerk count your cash. Let him work side by side with the clerk, weighing the coins in the scales, counting them, putting your hallmark on them, and storing them in your vaults. Keep him at this work a whole day. Then after that pick out some suitable person who has connections with his father in some way or other and invite him privately to your house. When he comes, say something like this to him:

"'My wife is just dying to have that man's second son as a son-in-law, though personally I can't see exactly what there is in him that attracts her so. It's not really urgent, but at your leisure if you'd sound him out as to whether or not he's interested in having my daughter as wife for his second son, I'd appreciate it very much. I can be perfectly frank with you. So let me say right out that no matter whom she marries, she'll have a dowry of a thousand pieces of silver.'

"After that, at the proper moment, when you think that enough time has elapsed for him to pass your message along to the man in question, let him know that you want to call in your loan to him. Without a doubt he will do everything in his power to repay you; because his love of money won't let him pass up the opportunity of welcoming into his household a bride with such a generous dowry. There's no other scheme but this that'll work."

Such was the gist of the advice given by the worldly-wise member of the One-Momme Club to his fellow financier, and then all the club members parted company.

On New Year's Eve that same year, the man who had loaned the money to the merchant comes to the one who has advised him as to the best method of recovering his loan. Smiling all over, he bows low before him, tapping his forehead with his fan, and says to him: "Thank you, thank you, thank you! It is due entirely to your good advice that just a few days ago I received not only the principal of my loan but the interest as well. Among us money-lenders such a resourceful man as yourself is indeed a rare jewel." Then, as he rises to leave, he says: "You recall that when you first advised me I promised to give you a *hiki* of pongee; however, I trust that this will do." So saying, he sets before him two *tan* of cheap paper cloth manufactured at Shiraishi. As he goes out he remarks over his shoulder, "As for that matter of the padding, we'll talk about that next spring."

IT'S EXPENSIVE TO LIE WHEN YOU'RE LYING LOW

EVERYONE was getting his forehead shaved and his hair dressed and donning holiday attire. So far as appearances went, a universal mood of festivity prevailed throughout the country in keeping with the New Year. But actually everybody was not facing the New Year in exactly the same fashion.

For example, there was one man who was so hard pressed that he determined not to pay any of his bills at all. On New Year's Eve, no sooner had he finished his breakfast than he put on his *haori,* and with his short sword at his side made ready to disappear temporarily. In an effort to placate his wife he said to her, "You must learn that above all the most important thing is perseverance. There will come a time," he continued, "when our circumstances will improve, and then you can ride about in a sedan chair. Remember, there's still some leftover duck meat from last night's supper. Warm it over, seasoning it with *sake,* and eat it. When the bill collectors come, pay them all the money there is in the house. But, mind you! Keep back one *kan* for your treasure-drawing game. When the money on hand is all gone, just let matters look after themselves, and lie in bed with your back to the bill collectors."

So speaking, the fellow hurriedly left home. Is it any wonder that the man was bankrupt? Seeing his funds grow shorter day after day, he had failed to come up with any ready plan to improve the situation. Woe to the wife of such a fellow: she looks old while not yet a mother. On this day of days, when every single *mon* counted, he put two or three one-*bu* coins and about thirty *momme* of silver in his purse and set out for a tavern which he'd never visited before.

"Oh," he said to the mistress as he entered the tavern, "you haven't settled your accounts yet, have you? Just look at all those bills, scattered about like a thousand letters. I'd say they must add up to two or three *kan*. Well, each household has its own expenses to meet, you know," he continued glibly. "Why, I've got to pay the draper alone six and a half *kan*. Pity a man whose wife is so extravagant. It would really be much better for me to get a divorce and spend what it costs to keep her on other women. Unfortunately, however, I can't do it because my wife became pregnant last March, and just this very morning her labor pains started. They say the baby will be born today, but even before it's born they're already making a great fuss over the choice of its swaddling clothes. They send for the wet nurse. Then midwives come—three or four of them. Then the family conjurer comes to charm and change the unborn infant from a girl into a boy. On top of that they have to prepare a bellyband, a cowrie shell, and a sea horse to be held in her left hand. The family doctor is busy in the next room boiling some birth-inducing herbs. Why, they even have stems of mushrooms ready, but goodness knows what they're for. Worst of all, my mother-in-law has just arrived, and she goes around poking her nose into everything, whether she's welcome or not. How utterly hilarious! Fortunately for me, however, they tell me I'm not supposed to be in the house; so I just dropped in here to pass the time away. Since you've never heard about my good fortune, I'm afraid you may think I'm here to escape the bill collectors, since it's New Year's Eve. But believe you me, I'm a man who owes nothing at all to anybody in this whole island. Do you mind if I stay here until the baby is born? I'll pay you in cash.

By the way, that yellowtail on the fish hanger is too small; it just won't do. Here; you'd better buy a bigger one right away." So saying, the customer plunked down a one-*bu* gold coin, which delighted the mistress no end and brought a smile on her face.

"How lucky!" she exclaimed. "I'll keep this a secret from my husband and buy an *obi* with it to satisfy a long-standing desire. It's really good luck to have such a generous customer as you to come in on New Year's Eve. It's a sure sign, I believe, we'll have good luck all next year. By the way, you're much too fine a fellow to stay here in the kitchen. Why don't you move into the regular room?" she urged him sweetly.

"Well, all right," he replied. "But just remember that I'm an awfully particular eater, altogether different from other people."

It was simply comical to see the way the mistress drew *sake* out of a special cask and warmed it up for him. After that, she tossed her hairpin on the floor for mat divination, and counted the number of seams from where it fell to the border of the mat, to see whether they were odd or even. Three times she tried, and each time the result came out the same, indicating for certain that the baby would be a boy. Thus the prediction of the mistress and the pure fabrication of the customer coincided perfectly.

To hum a popular song to the accompaniment of a woman's *samisen* at the year end, without regard to the convenience of the neighbors, is a form of amusement permitted only in the licensed quarters. In accord with the line of the song that runs so appropriately, "Leading a life of lamenting," most people of this world, with a load of care on their minds, come to the very last day of the year, only to discover that it is much too long. Ordinarily people regret the all too swift passage of the days, but this particular day is an exception. When it finally arrives, people usually wish just the opposite.

The entertainer who had been called into the inn for the customer's comfort feigned gaiety as part of her service. Although she did not feel happy, she spoke with a smile on her face: "What a pity it is that the years flit by one after another!" she said. "Last year the arrival of the New Year was delightful to me, for I could play battledore and shuttlecock, but now I'm nineteen years old. It won't be long before I'll have to sew up the slits in my *kimono* sleeves and be addressed as 'Madame.' I'm sorry to say that this may be the last year I'll be able to wear long-sleeved *kimono.*"

Unfortunately for the entertainer, the customer had a good memory, and replied, "The last time I met you at the Hanaya you were wearing *kimono* with round sleeves and saying you'd be nineteen that very day. That must have been about twenty years ago. So by now you must be at least thirty-nine, but you're still wearing long-sleeved *kimono*. What in the world could you have to regret? It's all to your advantage to be of small build, because it makes you look young." Thus unsparingly he reminded her of her old line of talk, while the woman could only sit quietly, with hands folded in apology. So the man gave up being particular about her age, and the two of them had a peaceful sleep in a friendly bed.

An old woman who seemed to be her mother appeared later, and called her out of the room. After mentioning one or two trivial things in conversation, the mother was then heard to remark that it was the last time she would see her daughter. For the want of fourteen or fifteen *momme* she was on her way to drown herself. On hearing this the younger woman burst into tears. Then she stripped off the padded silk *haori* she was wearing, wrapped it in a *furoshiki,* and gave it to her mother. The man was incapable of viewing this touching scene with indifference. So before the old woman left, once more a one-*bu* coin disappeared from his purse.

Feeling in high spirits after this bit of charity, his voice correspondingly rose higher. Now it happened that two servants of one of his creditors who were in the inn heard and recognized his voice. Whereupon they entered the room and cried out, "So here you are at last! We've been by your house several times since this morning, but each time we couldn't find you because you were out. Isn't it lucky we met you here!"

Then they transacted a bit of business with him. In the end, they relieved him of all his cash, together with his *haori,* his short sword, and one of his *kimono.* "And by January 5th," they reminded him as they left, "we'll expect you to pay the balance due."

The customer, though considerably out of countenance, managed to squeeze out a rather lame excuse. "I've got to see a friend of mine who has just sent word that he needs me to help him out," he explained. "In any case, it was injudicious of me to leave home on New Year's Eve." Thus putting up a front of respectability, he left the inn at daybreak. As he went off, the people in the tavern laughed and said, "Why, even a fool has more sense than that fellow!"

SENSIBLE ADVICE ON DOMESTIC ECONOMY

"The immutable rule in regard to the division of family property at the time of marriage," said the experienced go-between from Kyoto, "is as follows: Let us suppose that a certain man is worth a thousand *kan.* To the eldest son at his marriage will go four hundred *kan,* together with the family residence. The second son's share will be three hundred *kan,* and he too is entitled to a house of his own. The third son will be adopted into another family, requiring a portion of one hundred *kan.* If there is a daughter, her dowry will be thirty *kan,* in addition to a bridal trousseau worth twenty *kan.* It is advisable to marry her off to the son of a family of lower financial status. Formerly it was not unusual to spend forty *kan* on the trossseau and allot ten *kan* for the dowry, but because people today are more interested in cash, it is now customary to give the daughter silver in the lacquered chest and copper in the extra one. Even if the girl is so ugly that she can't afford to sit near the candle at night, that dowry of thirty *kan* will make her bloom into a very flowery bride!

"But be that as it may," continued the voice of experience, "there is certainly more to be said. Keep in mind that she is the spoiled darling of rich parents, accustomed to being fed on the choicest viands and daintiest morsels. Her round face with protruding cheekbones is really not so bad to look at after all. That bulging forehead, of course, will enable her to wear the bridal headdress more gracefully. Her wide-set nostrils are but a guarantee that she will never be short of breath. Her sparse hair will make it cool for her in summer. Her ample waistline will prove to be no drawback if she will only cover it with a magnificent over-garment. Her fat fingers will enable her to grasp all the more firmly the neck of the midwife.

"You see," argued the veteran of many a successful match, "it is possible to offer a plausible defense for any defect. In matchmaking, money is a very important consideration. If thirty *kan* of silver is deposited with a trustworthy merchant at six-tenths per cent interest per month, the income will total one hundred and eighty *momme* monthly, which will more than suffice to support four women: the bride, her personal maid, a second maid, and a seamstress. How unselfish must be the disposition of a bride who will not only look after the household faithfully, meantime taking care never to displease her husband's family, but also at the same time will actually pay for the food she eats! If you are looking merely for beauty, then go where women are made up solely to that end, to the licensed quarters. You are free to visit them any time of night you may wish, and thoroughly enjoy it, but next morning you will have to pay out seventy-one *momme*—which is not in the least enjoyable!

"A more thorough investigation will reveal the fact that the *sake* served at a brothel amounts to four *bu,* while in a house of ill fame the rice and tea consumed will cost eight *bu*. When you actually come to think of it," continued the man of experience, "you will realize that though the cost is exhorbitant it is but inevitable, for as with 'Baking pans of double price,' a margin to protect against loss must be added to the selling price. Not infrequently a customer will run out on his bill, in utter and base disregard for all sense of love and duty. Since it is impossible for the master to collect the money from him, his name will be crossed off his account book and the rascal himself given up as dead. Whereupon the master will solemnly strike the brazier with the fire tongs and utter a fearsome imprecation: 'May the gods damn him to the hell of starvation as punishment for his dishonesty! May all his baked ducks, his cedar-smoked roast fish, and every other delicacy he likes to order to appease his epicurean tastes, be burned to cinders, that he may be taught how terrible is the punishment for the crime of cheating on his debts!' This curse he utters with a look of horror, quite different from the expression on his face when receiving a striped *haori* made in the province of Hida.

"It is better on the whole," continued the wise old go-between, "to give up dissipation in good time, for a roué is seldom happy in later life. So even if life at home seems dry and tasteless, you'd better have patience with a supper of cold rice, potluck bean curd, and dried fish. You can always have one of your tenants repeat for you the story of Lord Itakura's gourd justice, just for the fun of it. Or you may lie down whenever you like, at perfect ease, and have a maid massage you down to the very tips of your toes. If you want tea, you may sip it while your wife holds the cup for you. A man in his own household is the commander supreme, whose authority none will dare to question, and there is none to condemn you. There's no need to seek further for genuine pleasure.

"Then, too, there are certain business advantages to staying home. Your clerks will stop their imprudent visits to the Yasaka quarters and their clandestine meetings at that rendezvous in Oike. And when in the shop, since they can't appear to be completely idle, maybe they'll look over those reports from the Edo branch office, or do some other work that they have been putting off doing—all to the profit of you, the master! The apprentice boys will diligently twist wastepaper into string, and in order to impress you, the master, sitting in the inner room, they will practice penmanship to their profit. Kyushichi, whose habit it is to retire early, will take the straw packing from around the yellowtail and make rope on which to string coins; while Take, in order to make things go more smoothly tomorrow, will prepare the vegetables for breakfast. The seamstress during the time you're at home will take off as many knots of Hino silk as she ordinarily does in a whole day. Even the cat keeps a wary watch in the kitchen and when she hears the least sound in the vicinity of the fish hanger she will mew to scare away the rats. If such unmeasured profit as this results from the master's remaining at home just one night, think how vast will be the benefits that will accrue within the space of a whole year! So even if you are not entirely satisfied with your wife, you have to exercise discretion and realize that in the gay quarters all is but vanity. For a young master to be well aware of this is the secret of the successful running of his household."

Such was the counsel offered by the veteran go-between from Kyoto on New Year's Eve. Though he dwelt upon it at some length, it was advice well worth listening to.

Be that as it may, let me say that the women of today, under the influence of the styles of the gay quarters, dress exactly like professional entertainers. Prominent drapers' wives, who in public are addressed as mesdames, are so attired as to be mistaken for high-class courtesans; while the wives of small shopkeepers, who once served as clerks of the drapers, look exactly like courtesans one grade lower. Again, the *kimono* worn by wives of tailors and embroiderers who live on side streets bear a startling resemblance to those of the women employed in teahouses. It is fun to spot them in a crowd dressed in conformity with their respective degrees of fortune.

A woman, after all, is only a woman: there are few, if any, marked differences between professionals and non-professionals. But by comparison the non-professionals seem slow-witted, ungainly, and unrefined in letter writing. Neither can they drink *sake* in nearly so graceful a manner as the professionals. Nor can they sing songs. They wear their *kimono* so clumsily that they seem to hang loose about them. They move so awkwardly that when walking down the street they're unsteady on their feet. In bed they can talk of nothing but bean paste and salt. They're so stingy that when blowing their nose they use only a single sheet of paper. They never even heard of aloeswood, thinking it might possibly be some kind of medicine. In any and in all respects they are disappointing, and even in their hair styles, which are copied after those of professional courtesans, there is a world of difference.

Any courtesan-chaser must be an exceptionally smart fellow. Despite his cleverness, however, and his knowledge that money is hard to earn, he won't pay his debts though urgently pressed to do so—not even when he is under indictment for non-payment. Yet he dares to reserve the services of his favorite courtesan for the entire New Year's season, in utter disregard of the cost. He will even pay in advance the whole bill as early as December 13th, the very first day of the preparation season for the New Year. Shrewd though this fellow is about many things, he is blinded by the pleasures he finds in the gay quarters.

A prosperous merchant of Karasuma Street, Kyoto, on retiring from business, gave to each of his two sons five hundred *kan*. The younger son steadily increased his wealth, until all his relatives believed that he was worth two thousand *kan*. As for the elder son, when New Year's Eve rolled around in the fourth year of his independence, he felt compelled to utter a fervent prayer of thanksgiving to God that the night was dark. Had the moon been shining brightly, the memory of his former respectability would never have allowed him to walk the streets of Kyoto selling pepper. Under cover of darkness, with head and face concealed in a paper hood, he wandered about unnoticed, a poor peddler of pepper, till the New Year dawned upon him. The place to which his aimless feet had carried him was none other than the Tamba Highway, which was also the entrance to the Shimabara gay quarter. Memories of better days came back to him, when he used to enter that very gate at dawn. But now he had to turn his weary footsteps homeward.

LIFE AND DOORPOSTS: BOTH ARE BORROWED

Generally speaking, when we get accustomed to something, it no longer worries us. At the entrance of Shimabara, the notorious gay quarter of the capital, there is a certain stretch of rice field, through which runs the 'Lane of Shusaka,' famous in the popular ballad. In autumn when the rice is ripening, the farmers make a scarecrow to frighten the birds away. They set it up in the field with an old sedge-straw hat on its head and a bamboo stick in its hand. But as the kites and crows are used to seeing the great sedge hats with the familiar shop brands on them, worn by those pleasure seekers who visit the quarter, they are no longer scared away, probably taking the scarecrow to be some lone pleasure seeker. By and by they even dare to perch on the hat, treating the straw man as just another stray man-about-town.

In this world there is surely nothing more terrible than an encounter with a bill collector. Yet even in this, when one has become accustomed over the years to being in debt, he is not to be intimidated even on New Year's Eve.

A veteran debtor was proudly boasting one New Year's Eve: "Nobody has ever had his head cut off for failing to pay a debt. Not that I won't pay so long as I am able. But you can't get blood out of a turnip. How I wish I had a money tree! But sad to say there's none at hand for I never sowed the seed."

So saying he spread out an old straw mat in the sun near a tree in the corner of his garden, and sat him down upon it, holding a well-sharpened fish knife in his hand. "I've gone to great pains to whet this knife, but now there's nothing to cut with it. Not even a tiny bit of sardines! Still it may serve some useful purpose. At any moment now I may wax so indignant that I'll kill myself. After all, our passing moods are of such a nature that we can't control them forever. Through fifty-six years I've lived my life, but now I'm no longer attached to it. It's a pity that in Kyoto's most exclusive residential sections so many potbellied plutocrats die young. I swear by the Fox God that if only one of them would pay off all my debts for me I'd gladly die in his stead by committing *harakiri*."

Thus speaking, he brandished his blade and looked exactly as though he himself were possessed by a fox. At this very moment along came a clucking hen. "Come," he called to her, "I'll take you along with me on my journey into the next world." With a single sweep of his sharp blade he sliced off her head.

Seeing this, the bill collectors who had been waiting about were suddenly seized with fright. Next thing they knew he'd be picking a quarrel with them on the very slightest pretext. So one after another they took their leave. On parting, however, they did not forget to speak words of consolation to the debtor's wife, who had begun to kindle a fire under the teakettle. They expressed profound sympathy that she was so unfortunate as to be the wife of so short-tempered a fellow.

To resort to such a dodge as this to be rid of bill collectors at the end of the year was nothing new; it was, however, a mean trick. Nevertheless, by this means the old reprobate was able to tide over his year-end financial embarrassment without uttering a single word of apology to anyone.

There remained, however, one young apprentice to a timber dealer in Horikawa Street who had not taken his leave with the other bill collectors. Being only eighteen or nineteen years old, he looked both weak and womanish, but his heart was as strong as a lion's. All the while the seasoned debt dodger had been playing out his little drama, the young apprentice had been lingering on the bamboo veranda, unconcernedly telling the beads of his rosary. When the last of the others had disappeared, he spoke up with great deliberation: "Now that the show's over, I'd like to get my bill paid and be on my way."

"What!" cried the debtor. "Even the grown-ups were taken in completely and have gone their way, but here you sit and even dare to condemn my conduct as a mere act. Just what do you mean by this, anyhow?"

"At a time like this," replied the apprentice, "when we're all so busy, I consider that little act of yours to be an unnecessary trick."

"Mind your own business!" exploded the angry debtor. "I'm not leaving here until I get . . ."

"Get what!" shouted the thoroughly angry fellow.

" . . . get my money," calmly finished the apprentice.

"From whom?" came the angry retort.

"From anybody who owes me money," replied the self-possessed apprentice. "If need be, I'll take the money from him by force. I'm an expert, you know, at this sort of thing. Among all my fellow bill collectors, none would even attempt to collect from this list of twenty-seven notorious debtors. Take a look at this account book I have here. So far I've checked off the names of twenty-six and I've no intention of quitting here until I've collected your debt. Until you have paid your bill, the timbers you used to repair your house belong to us. So I'll carry them off with me."

Suiting action to words, the young apprentice forthwith took up his sledge hammer and began tearing out the doorposts of the house.

Whereupon the master of the house jumped up and rushed toward him, crying out, "You rascal! I won't stand for such an insult."

"Come, come," replied the apprentice in a mollifying tone of voice, "the style of your threat is out of date. You seem to be completely ignorant of the current fashion. To tear out doorposts is the very latest thing in effective bill collecting."

Since the young man showed no signs whatever of being frightened by his threats, there was nothing left for the old debtor to do but apologize to him and pay in full the overdue bill.

When the young apprentice had checked the last of the twenty-seven names off his list of unpaid accounts, he turned to the now thoroughly subdued debtor and said, "Now that I've been paid there's nothing further to say. However, let me tell you this much anyhow. Your entire technique of resistance is quite passé. Experienced old campaigner that you are, your style is definitely dated. It would be much better if you'd coach your wife well in advance. Start your quarrel with her about noon on New Year's Eve. Have her change her *kimono*, all the while crying out: 'Any moment now I'm ready to get a divorce from you. But I warn you that if it comes to this, several people will die. Do you understand this thoroughly? It's no laughing matter in the least.' Then at this point you ought to interrupt her and say, 'How dare you divorce me? You haven't the courage'. 'Oh, yes?' she'll reply. 'I certainly have. And there's nothing going to stop me!' Now at this point you appear to back water. You say to her, 'How I've yearned to pay my debts so when I die people'll speak well of me, for the proverb says, "Man is mortal but fame is lasting." Much as I regret it, this has come to pass. There's nothing I can do about it. This very day will be my last on this earth. Oh, what a pity!' Lamenting after this fashion, then, you ought to grab some papers—any old worthless paper will do. Tear them into shreds one after another, just as though they were valuable documents. When they see you do this, even the most obstinate of bill collectors will give up and no longer press for payment."

Having listened attentively to the advice of the young apprentice, the old debtor spoke: "That's a trick I've never tried. Now, thanks to your suggestion I'll win through the next year end." Turning to his wife he asked, "What do you think of it, my dear? Isn't it a wonder that a lad so young should show a wisdom so superior to my own? An occasion such as this calls for a celebration."

Quickly the hen slain shortly before was converted into soup, and then, with the apprentice boy an honored guest, the two ate the dinner to celebrate the successful end of the year.

The meal done and the boy gone, the old veteran had second thoughts: "It's not just the next year end that we must watch," he cogitated. "Those persistent bill collectors will be assaulting us again before the new year dawns." Immediately he began mapping out with his wife the strategy they would employ in their rehearsed quarrels.

So competently did he manage to deal with the bill collectors by means of his newly acquired technique that thereafter his fame spread abroad as the 'Quarreler of Omiya Street.'

THE OPENING PERFORMANCE BY THE NEW PLAYERS

IN THE THEATERS of Kyoto it is customary to perform as a prelude to the opening of a performance, a dance to congratulate the city on its prosperity. Indeed, the townspeople of Kyoto, just like the merchants of the capital city, are as generous as generous can be when occasion demands, which is due entirely to their never-ending figuring and the economy-minded living of their lives day by day.

Several years ago in Kyoto in the fall, the Komparu School from Kaga Province announced the opening of a Noh play performance. It was to run for four days, and although the price of theater boxes was set at ten pieces of silver, they were soon sold out. Furthermore, cash in advance was paid for them.

At first it was announced that the tragic drama *Sekidera Komachi* would be presented, and people were greatly excited in expectation of witnessing a performance of this grandest of dramas. But when the hand drummer, for some reason or other, found it impossible to perform his part, the program was changed. Despite the alteration, however, on the opening day even before dawn, people thronged the entrance to the theater. Among them was a man from Edo who had reserved two entire boxes, each of which had cost him ten pieces of silver. In one of them he spread out a crimson rug, and further equipped it with a portable shelf, a low folding screen, and a case for his personal effects. In the back of the box he set up a temporary kitchen, provided with fish, fowl, and a basket of seasonal fruit. In the other box he set up a teakettle, with two pails of water beside it for making tea, one labeled 'Uji Bridge' and the other 'Otowa River.' Seated with him in his boxes were to be seen a physician, a draper, a Confucian scholar, a dealer in imported goods, and a poet; while visible behind them were women from Shimabara, boys from Shijo, prominent entertainers of the city, a masseur, and a *ronin.* Under the boxes was space for his personal palanquin, a bath, and even a lavatory. Indeed, with such luxurious appointments nothing at all was lacking in convenience for the enjoyment of the play.

Such was the magnanimity of this man from Edo. Yet he was not the son of a feudal lord; he had attained to his position of eminence solely by dint of his wealth. Which is a very good reason why you should make money above all things else, in order that you too might disport yourself as you please. But there was method in this man's madness about the theater, for he was very careful in all his entertaining to see that his wealth suffered no impairment. When business is combined with pleasure, how enjoyable it is! If a man is not rich enough, however, he should under no circumstances spend money wastefully.

When the season end of September is past, it seems to be the usual custom for people to relax their attention to business, for then the year end still seems to be a thing of the distant future. With the coming of October, however, the weather changes: it becomes unsettled, and the rain and the winds threaten. In such an atmosphere as this it seems only natural for people to become nervous and restless. They tend to postpone until spring any particular thing they may have been planning, and they make shift with the bare necessities of daily life. Under such conditions they give up any ideas they might have had about buying luxuries or the works of artists. By and by, when the morning frost and the evening blasts drive them early to bed and near to the fireplace provided for their comfort during winter's confinement, they are again liable to neglect their business, and as a result they may come to the end of the year hard pressed.

Later on there will follow, one after the other, the anniversary of the founder of the Buddhist sect of Nichiren, the series of ten evening sermons by the Jodo sect, the anniversary honoring the founder of the Tofukuji Temple, as well as that of the founder of the Ikko sect. The daytime festival and the evening merrymaking for the Day of the Boar come close together, only to be followed shortly by the bonfire ceremony at the Inari Shinto Shrine.

Likewise about this time of year, the members of the theatrical troupe of Shijo River Beach are changed, and the first performance of the new troupe is staged. Actors of long-standing reputation appear to be new, and people in general become optimistic. They tell each other how today they will attend Theater A, tomorrow Theater B, and the next day Theater C, for that's where they'll see the young actors from Osaka playing. And through the medium of the teahouse attached to the theater they reserve box seats, and give generous tips to their favorite actors, that they might be hailed as their 'patrons'—a very hollow and useless vanity indeed!

Drunk with the *sake* they have brought into the theater, they do not return straight home after the performance, but linger to watch the epilogue dance again in the upstairs room in Ishigake Street. So boisterously do they talk and so uproariously do they carouse that one would fear they could be heard all the way to the top of Mt. Hiei. As these carousers are prominent people in Kyoto, however, other people talk about them: "Oh, yes! He's the favorite draper of Mr. So-and-So," or, "He's the broker that has entree to Lord What-You-May-Call-'im's house." To be thus gossiped about is considered by these habitués of the gay quarter to be an honor.

However, in the case of a merchant with little capital, the story is entirely different. If he attends the theater just to beguile the time, he must be careful not to sit next to a smoker, lest the craving to smoke overcome him; and as for a cushion for his seat—well, he had better rent one made of straw. Still, from where he sits he can learn the names of the actors just as easily as anybody else.

Now on the very opening day, when Yojibei and his troupe staged their new program, several young fellows, whose appearance indicated that they cared not a straw whether or not they were disinherited, were seen to be seated to the left of the stage. Being fashionably dressed, they were played up to by the actors on the stage, to the great envy of all the spectators. Seated in the audience, however, was one man who happened to have inside information about them, and he revealed their stories as follows:

"Though I don't know exactly how rich or how poor they are, I do know this: they are people from the River West section of the city. Isn't it amusing to see them putting on as grand airs as the people of the Mid-City? Why, a stranger might mistake them for men of distinction. That fellow dressed in the black *haori* married the heiress of a rice dealer, strictly from mercenary motives. His wife must be fourteen or fifteen years older than he is. He makes his old mother grind rice in a hand mill, and he sets his younger brother to tramping about the streets of Kyoto selling horse beans. He ought to quit wearing that white-hilted sword.

"That fellow wearing the iridescent *haori* is a glue dealer of uncertain origin, though from his gay clothes you might suppose he was more respectable than he is. His house is mortgaged and people say he can't keep up the payments on it. Besides, he has a dispute over the eastern boundary line with his neighbor that, because of his obstinacy, has not been settled yet. At such a critical time as this, it is sheer madness for him to show up in the theater.

"That third fellow over there in the whitish-brown *haori* is known to have borrowed five *kan*—not without paying interest, of course,—for a dowry that would enable him to become the adopted heir of a lacquerer. His foster father hasn't been dead thirty-five days, yet here he sits in the theater, leaving his poor widowed mother alone at home. What an uncouth fellow he is! At a time when no merchant in Kyoto is willing to sell him rice, or fuel, or any other daily necessity on credit, he calls in gay boys to entertain him while he's on a spree. Poor lads, they think he's a rich patron, because it's humanly impossible for them to find out the truth about him. Quite contrary to their belief, though, he hasn't paid for any credit purchases for the past several years.

"That fellow wearing the colored striped *haori* runs a small exchange shop. His brother is a priest in the Miidera Temple, and if he doesn't come to his financial aid, he won't be able to scrape past the year end. Except for him, not a single one of them will be able to stay in the capital to celebrate the New Year."

As he spoke, he pointed in their direction and laughed; whereupon, misinterpreting it as an expression of envy, they took two or three cumquats, and, placing them on camellia and daffodil leaves, wrapped them up in paper and tossed them over in his direction. Opening up the package, our narrator smiled in derision and remarked, "If they were really what they pretend to be, they would have paid two *bu* for each single cumquat. But you may be sure they'll never pay that price."

By and by the entire program ended and our running

commentator took his leave and went home. Thereafter the same crowd appeared at the theater day after day, but always dressed in the same clothes and wearing the identical *haori*. When the teahouse manager noticed it, he at once asked them to pay their bills. But they declined to do so, and after that they abruptly ceased coming to the theater. Till the end of the year he continued to dun them, but all in vain.

Then one of them, despising moonlight flitting as out-of-date, took to coming out in broad daylight, still flitting about to no one knew where. Another was confined to his room on the pretext of being insane. Still another, who tried to commit suicide, was thereafter kept under observation. As for the entertainer who had introduced these fellows to the teahouse, he was put under police surveillance for having endorsed thieves.

The teahouse keeper, who could think of nothing to do but despair of ever collecting his money, finally managed to persuade himself that it was all a horrible nightmare and beat a hasty retreat. Whereas he had anticipated earning fifteen *ryo* from them, all that remained with him after the episode were three sedge hats left behind and the rather painful proof that on New Year's Eve he was the biggest dupe in Kyoto.

HOW LOVELY THE SIGHT OF RICE-CAKE FLOWERS AT NEW YEAR'S

On New Year's Eve the bill collectors must be quite familiar with that old saying, 'Be quick to do good,' for they surely move around swiftly. On this special day they speed about the world like so many wing-footed Mercuries, till it seems that their sandals, though made of iron, would be completely worn out. Indeed, to the merchants their vitality means everything. By the way, I once heard an old bill collector give the following advice:

"To be successful in collecting bills you must start with the one who pays most readily and then work up to the hard one who is notorious for nonpayment. Be careful not to trip over your own tongue. If the debtor behaves in a manner calculated to irritate you, remain all the calmer and speak only of the matter at hand, and that with a persuasive tongue. Sit down on the threshold in a leisurely manner, tell your porter to put out the light, and talk in a way similar to this:

" 'What crime did I commit in a former life that I should have been condemned to suffer in this one as a bill collector? I have yet to celebrate New Year's Day even once with my hair done up properly. My wife has to work in a banker's office, a virtual hostage, where she has to try to please even the clerks. Of all the hundreds of possible ways to earn a living, why should I ever have chosen such a mode of life as this? Sometimes I feel like reproaching the tutelary god, even though I know he hasn't anything to do with my present sorry lot.

" 'In contrast, though I'm a stranger to your household affairs, I'm sure the mistress lacks nothing to make her happiness complete. Those lovely rice-cake flowers hanging from the ceiling are full of the rejoicing of the New Year season. And by the way, that fish hanger over there is the most attractive thing in the house. Oh, just look at the duck, and the dried sea cucumbers, and the dried sea ears hanging there. I'm sure you've already prepared your winter wardrobe. The patterns in vogue now with the ladies are peonies with leaves intertwined with four ginkgo leaves combined in a circle. I wish my wife could afford to wear fashionable and up-to-date *kimono*. It's so true that clothes make the woman. Say, O-Matsu! The *kimono* the master gave you must be patterned with pale blue paulownia flowers against a dark brown background. You are lucky to be working in this house. Out on the edge of town I see many women wearing *kimono* of old-fashioned arabesque design.'

"Talking in this fashion, you must strive to create a leisurely atmosphere, in order to induce the wife to say something. Then, when the other bill collectors are not around, the master of the house will quietly come to you and say that although he is determined not to pay anybody else this year end, yet because he admires your reasonable conversational approach he'll pay you this much, even though it's the money he's saved up for his wife's pilgrimage to the Grand Shrine at Ise. The balance he will pay you before next March, when he hopes to see your smiling face again.

"So saying, he will pay you sixty *momme* out of a hundred due. In olden times they used to pay eighty *momme* out of a hundred. Twenty years ago they would have paid half the debt without fail. Ten years ago a forty-percent payment was prevalent, but nowadays they will pay only thirty *momme* out of a hundred, which usually includes at least two bad pieces of silver. Thus men's minds grow more and more debased, and such is the situation existing between creditor and debtor. What a nuisance to the creditor! But for him there is no escape from it unless he goes out of business, which he cannot afford to do. Whereupon, forgetting the troubles of the year end, he will again start selling to customers on credit.

"It is fascinating how customs change with the times. In olden times the creditor accepted the debtor's excuse for failure to pay up and after midnight on New Year's Eve stopped trying to collect bills overdue. Later, when collectors persevered until dawn, quarrels broke out wherever they went. Quite recently, although collections are made far into the wee hours of the morning, no angry words arise between creditor and debtor, for all is settled without too much fuss.

"Just how is it settled that way? 'The truth is that where there's no money, there's just no money to be got,' declares the debtor, not afraid to be overheard by his neighbors. 'Why, even the feudal lords are in debt nowadays! No one's been beheaded yet for failure to pay his debts, even though they may amount to a thousand *kan*. If I really had any money to pay, I wouldn't put you off. Oh, how I wish this cauldron were filled with one-*bu* silver pieces! Then I could clear off all my debts at once. Actually, money is the most biased thing I know; it actually seems to hate me.'

"So speaking, he will then break into a song from a Noh play, singing, 'Now you are up, then you are down. That's the way of the world.' Meantime, while stretched at full length on the floor, he beats time on his wooden pillow like a hand drum.

"That sort of fellow is simply beyond me! Since he defies all sense of shame and decency, the average bill collector figures it will simply be a waste of time to talk with him any further; so he strikes off his old credits and discounts the new ones. Thus the two reach an amicable compromise instead of continuing to quarrel. Today people have grown wiser."

When you consider carefully the state of the world, you will realize that it is better to have a foolish son than a smart clerk, for the son is by nature honest. When he sets out to collect bills he never does the job halfheartedly, for he knows that the money will be his own some day. On the contrary, the young employee with sincere regard for his master, who attends to his duties faithfully and understands his position, is rather an exception, for rare indeed is the employee who is devoted to his master's interests. He would prefer to visit the gay quarter, where each day a thousand pieces of gold are squandered. If he collects a fair sum of money, he pilfers some, entering it in his notebook as 'short.' Or he may surreptitiously exchange good gold for bad, or substitute copper for silver, and misappropriate the financial profit gained thereby to his own personal uses. Those credits of which the master is ignorant he may possibly enter as 'non-collectable.' Even the shrewdest master cannot keep up with all the varied forms of embezzlement.

In the case of a petty merchant's apprentice, he too fails to pay sincere attention to his bill collecting. Instead, he buys cards at the Hoteiya shop and walks along the street trying to memorize them, at a time when he ought to be busy working. Anyway, his actions are of no profit to his master.

Bill collectors are not all of the same disposition, but good-natured ones are rare. Hence it is of great importance to be on guard all day long, considering every man to be a robber, just as truly as fire is caused by the careless handling of fuel.

Once there lived a certain Churoku whose nickname was 'Demosthenes.' He worked as foreman at a building site, and since he was forever cracking jokes he gained the reputation of being the town's chief unofficial entertainer. His mimicry unfailingly pleased the company at such meetings as that of the Moon-Waiting Society or the Day-Waiting Club. Now it happened one year that as the new year approached, he found that he would be hard pressed to tide over the year end. So he went to the home of one of his patrons and asked him for a loan of five hundred *momme* of silver. His request being quickly granted, he was so delighted that he returned after dark to his patron's house and sat down on the floor to sing a song of appreciation and congratulation:

SONG OF CHUROKU ON NEW YEAR'S EVE

How merry the notes of the *koto*
  That fall this eve on my ears!
'Tis the house of one blest by the *kami,*
  A demigod, free from all cares.

In all the wide city of Osaka,
  There's no other house, far or near,
That with silver and gold is surrounded,
  With treasures which none can compare,

With the cloak that makes you invisible,
  And the hat that makes you the same.
Oh, the hammer that fashioned the money scale's beam
  Was Daikoku's mallet of fortune and fame.

How blest is my master!

On hearing the voice raised in song the master entered and said, "Churoku, you seem to be waiting to see me. Is it for this?" So saying, he tossed him five hundred *momme* wrapped up in a sheet of paper. Cuhroku raised it to his forehead thrice, each time repeating appropriate expressions of gratitude. "Thanks to you," he said with feeling, "I shall now be able to tide over the year end. I'll take my leave now, for before long the cock will be crowing." When he got as far as the doorway, he trotted back to ask the maids to tell the mistress how grateful he was. Whereupon one of them, Kichi by name, reminded him that this was a most auspicious season. "You're right!" he said gaily, "so I'll try a dance."

While Churoku was in the midst of his dance of felicitation, the head clerk of the household suddenly returned from business in the northern district and as he entered the house he cried out, "We must send two hundred *kan* to the warehouse office at once. The rice will be arriving any minute. Cash, cash! We are badly in need of cash. This is not the time for play and song, even by you women. Somehow we'll have to raise that cash."

At this moment his eye happened to light on the five hundred *momme* which Churoku had left on the threshold when he began his long dance. He snatched it up, crying, "Oh, what a lot of money we have here! How dare anyone leave it lying around so carelessly? Two hundred *kan* in cash is the money we need. Let's see whether or not we have that much in the house. If not, we'll have to send out search parties to scour the city until we raise it. O money, money, money! My kingdom for some money!"

The clerk had created such a furor that poor Churoku was completely nonpulsed. So with empty hands he beat a hasty retreat.

GOLDEN DREAMS

"DON'T forget your business," admonished a millionaire, "even in your dreams." For in your sleep you are sure to dream of what gives you most concern. Sometimes the dreams are happy, sometimes they are sad. One of the most common of them is that of finding money by the roadside. But nowadays no one would ever lose his pocketbook, for he cares as much for it as he does for his life. No, you couldn't find even a farthing in the vicinity of a temple where the Ten-Thousand-Day Service has just been held, nor even on the very next day after the Temma Festival. The fact is that money won't come to you unless you work for it.

There was a certain poor fellow of Fushimi who longed to become rich all at one jump, although he habitually neglected his work day by day. He had formerly lived in Edo, where in those days loose silver could be seen piled up in the money exchange shops in Suruga Street. Such a vivid impression had it made upon his mind that he still recalled the sight.

"Oh, how I wish I owned such a heap of silver at this year end!" he sighed to himself. "There was also a newly minted stack of gold lying on the counting board that was as high as my head," and he lay back on his paper-covered bed, obsessed with his thoughts of money.

On the very last day of December his wife awoke at dawn. Glancing in the direction of a sunbeam that had just come peeping in through the eastern window, she saw, to her great amazement, a heap of gold. "Oh, my goodness!" she cried aloud, awakening her husband. "This is literally a gift from heaven!"

"What's the matter?" he asked drowsily. But at that very instant, much to her great disappointment the gold disappeared. When she told him what she had seen, her husband remarked, "The temporary manifestation of gold to you must have been caused by my attachment to all that money I saw when we were living in Edo. My situation is so hopeless at present that I would gladly toll the bell of damnation at Nakayama in Sayo. I wish I could be saved from poverty in this present world, even though it might mean damnation for me in the next. Why, in this present life rich people enjoy a veritable paradise, while we poor people suffer the very tortures of hell. We have absolutely nothing! Not even a stick of firewood to burn in the stove. Oh, what a miserable way to end the year!"

Even as such wicked desires arose in his mind, his soul was changed from good to evil. When he fell into a doze, he dreamed of the black and white messengers of hell, drawing a rumbling fiery cart behind them, and pointing out to him the boundary line between his world and theirs. When he awoke and told his wife of the dream, she grew all the sadder and thus admonished him:

"No one can live to be a hundred. So it is unwise of you to entertain such a silly desire. In future, if our love for each other does not diminish a bit but remains constant, we can hope to celebrate New Year's Day happily. I can well imagine how it must vex you sometimes when you think what I have to put up with. But if things continue as bad as they are now, the three of us will starve to death.

"It's fortunate for us that I now have an offer of employment. It will also be a good thing for the future of our only son. If you will be so kind as to bring him up with your own hand, we may still look forward to happiness at some future time. I know it's cruel of me to desert him, but please take good care of him for me." All the while she spoke she was choking with tears, which so overwhelmed her husband with grief that he could say not a word in reply, but shut his eyes against the tears, unable to look her in the face.

Just then a woman business agent from Sumizome arrived at the house, in company with an old woman about sixty years old. "As I was telling you yesterday," she said to the young mother, "you have good breasts; so you will be paid the whole eighty-five *momme* in cash, and in addition you may have new *kimonos* made for you four times a year. You ought to be grateful for such generous treatment. Why, the pay of a kitchen maid as tall as a tower, who does the weaving in addition to her regular work, is only thirty-two *momme* every six months. It's because of your breasts, you know, that you are being paid so well. If you turn down this offer, I have another candidate for the job in the upper part of Kyomachi Street. Anyway," she concluded, " since we must have a wet nurse beginning today, you'll have to make up your mind."

Speaking in a spirit of self-sacrifice the wife replied, "It's only because we don't want to starve. Now my chief concern is whether or not I'll be able to do my duty successfully to the beloved son of my new master. In any case, I sincerely desire to work for him."

"Then let's start as soon as possible," replied the agent, completely ignoring the husband. She then borrowed a brush and ink from the next-door neighbor, wrote out a contract for a year, and handed her the sum of money in cash. At the same time, however, she shrewdly kept back her commission of eight and a half *momme* out of the money envelope on which was written "Eighty-five *momme;* thirty-seven pieces." "It's all the same whether I take it out now or later," she said defensively. "Anyhow, this is what everybody does."

"And now, my dear nurse," continued the agent, "I repeat, there's no need to stop to change clothes." And she started to leave at once. The husband was dissolved in tears. The wife, also flushed with weeping, spoke to her baby, saying, "Goodbye, Big Man. Mama is now leaving to go to her new master's home, but some day during the New Year's season she will come back to see you." She then asked her neighbors to take good care of her baby, and once again burst into tears.

Altogether unmoved by what she witnessed, the woman business agent hardheartedly declared, "Babies can grow up without parents. If one is not going to die, he won't die even if you beat him to death. So long, mister!" And so saying, she walked on off. However, the old woman who had come along with her was moved with compassion. She looked back toward the poor husband and baby and sighed, "He will love his baby just as I love my grandson. It's a pity to see an infant deprived of its mother's breasts." The agent, with no regard for the feelings of the mother who stood beside her, called back to the old woman, "It can't be helped, for money runs this world. It's really no concern of ours whether that baby lives or dies." And so saying, and stonyhearted as ever, she hurried away with the mother.

Meantime the evening came on, the eve of New Year's Day. The poor fellow, left at home and thoroughly sick of life, mumbled to himself, "I inherited a considerable fortune, but because of my bad management I lost it all and had to leave Edo. It was due solely to my wife's considerate efforts that I was able to settle down here in Fushimi. Even if we should have nothing but 'good-luck tea' to toast the parting year, we could still be happy if only we could celebrate the New Year's Day together. Oh, what a shame!"

In expectation of eating *zoni* with his wife on New Year's Day the man had bought two pairs of chopsticks. When his glance happened to fall on them lying on a corner of the shelf he picked one up and said, "One pair is unnecessary now," and so saying he broke the chopsticks in two and threw the pieces into the kitchen fire.

When night fell, the baby began to cry and would not be comforted. The wives of the neighbors came in and showed him how to put *jio* in the ricepaste and water, and how to warm it up and feed it to the baby through a bamboo tube. "It may just be my imagination," remarked one of the women, "but it seems to me by the looks of his chin that this baby has lost flesh even in a single day."

"I couldn't help it," thought the man to himself. And then all of a sudden, feeling very angry with no one in particular, he hurled the firetongs he held in his hand out into the garden. Seeing him in such agony, the wives said to one another, "Here sits a poor unhappy husband, while his wife is enjoying herself. Her new master likes to have a good-looking maid around the house, especially since she looks so much like his wife who died recently. Why, if you saw her from the back, you'd say she looks just as attractive as his dead wife did."

That did it!

No sooner had the husband heard this remark than he snatched up the money from where it had been lying untouched ever since his wife had left home, and rushed out of the house. For now he felt that he would rather die of starvation than be separated from her a moment longer.

So he brought his wife back home, and they celebrated the arrival of the New Year, in tears—but together!

EVEN GODS MAKE MISTAKES SOMETIMES

ANNUALLY in October all the gods from each province in Japan meet at the Grand Shrine of Izumo to discuss the peace and welfare of the people. At that time also the year gods are assigned to their appointed places to speed preparations for the coming New Year. The foremost in virtue, to be sure, are chosen to look after Kyoto, Edo, and Osaka. Veteran gods are likewise assigned to Nara and Sakai; while appropriate gods are designated for Nagasaki, Otsu, and Fushimi. Other suitable gods are selected for appointment to castle towns where feudal lords reside, to seaports, and to the chief inland towns and mountain villages. It is the task of the gods, besides, to see that the New Year comes to even the lowliest who live in the most distant isles or the poorest huts: to each and everyone, in fact, who makes up ricecakes and sets out pine branches before his doorway.

Now so far as preference goes, the gods themselves would much rather be the year gods of urban districts, for they dislike having to preside over the New Year festivities in rural areas. In any case, when a choice is given between town and country, it goes without saying that in every respect the former is preferable.

Time flows by as swiftly as the current of a stream, and all too soon comes the last day of December. Here in the city of Sakai people are careful of their fortunes, always figuring out ways to protect them. Everyone puts on an appearance of living more simply than he actually does. From the outside his house is latticed in front like that of a retired merchant, but inside it is wide and spacious.

He never fails to estimate his annual income, and to live within it.

Suppose a man has a daughter. After she is over the smallpox, he gauges how beautiful or ugly she is, and if he thinks that she might blossom into a woman of passable beauty, even though she is but four or five years old, he will start accumulating her trousseau, piece by piece and year after year. If the daughter happens to be plain in appearance, he knows that no young man will marry her without a dowry. Therefore he loans out money on interest, or he takes up some sideline, in order to earn some extra money against the time of her marriage. This shows the sort of perspicacious fellow he is.

As a result of his foresightedness, room after room is added to his house, and before the roof becomes too old he has it reshingled. He also reinforces the beams with stone foundations before they rot away. He likewise keeps an eye on the copper gutters, and several years before he is forced to repair them, he begins a wary watch on the ups and downs of the copper market, and when the price of copper is at the bottom he has his gutters repaired. The hand-woven suit of pongee that he wears every day will not become threadbare because he never moves about hastily. His clothes, therefore, give him the appearance of a gentleman, and yet at the same time they are quite economical. He is possessed of many household things that have been handed down from one generation to the next; so when he sets out to give a year end tea, publicly he gives the impression of living a life of luxury, yet actually it doesn't cost him very much. Such are the practices of one who has managed to live in the world for a good many years.

If even rich men must practice economy, how much more essential is it for those who are not very rich. Instead of sleeping on a pillow at night he ought to rest his head on an abacus, aware even in his sleep that the approaching year end may either make him or break him. If he would like to view red maple leaves in the fall, he ought to make good use of his imagination which will enable him to see them in the cheap red rice he pounds in his hand mortar. Instead of himself eating red porgy at cherry-blossom time, he might be better advised to send it to Kyoto, where the demand for it is so great. Nay, he ought never to buy even a river carp, giving as an excuse that it smells of mud, except, of course, when he has a guest to entertain. Kyoto is surrounded by mountains, yet the people who live there eat bonito; while the people who live near the sea are content to eat smaller fish. As the proverb goes, "It is darkest at the foot of the lighthouse."

One fact of life is that things are not always what they seem to be. One New Year's Eve, the assigned year god entered the home of a certain prosperous-looking merchant unannounced, to receive honors in celebration of the New Year, for such is the prerogative of all the year gods. In this house the New Year shelf was prepared, but there was no offertory light burning on it. There was an ominous and deserted air about the place. Nevertheless, since it was the house of his choice, and moreover, as it was inadvisable to share the entertainment with another god, which would be more than likely if he moved to another house, he remained where he was, rather curious to see just how the master would celebrate the New Year.

Now every time the door was opened, he could hear the mistress timidly repeating the same apology that her husband had not yet come home and that she was sorry the caller had come in vain so often. In the meantime midnight came and went and the dawn drew near. But still the bill collectors continued to arrive at the house one after another and began to bellow: "How soon will the master be back?" Whereupon the clerk came rushing up out of breath and reported thus: "As we were hurrying along about midway to Sukematsu, several rogues of towering height suddenly fell upon us and carried the master off into a pine grove, and began to threaten him to choose between his money and his life. I barely managed to escape from them."

"You coward!" the mistress exclaimed, appearing to be greatly astonished. "Shame upon your manhood for forsaking your master in his hour of peril when his life was at stake." Seeing her dissolved in tears, the bill collectors left the place one by one. By and by the sky began to grow brighter. When the last bill collector had disappeared, the sadness of the mistress, strangely enough, appeared to do the same. Then the clerk took out a bag of money and said to her, "The country people are pinched for money too; I was able to collect only thirty-five *momme* of silver and six hundred *momme* of copper." This clerk, employed in an artful and contriving household, was himself no slouch when it came to money matters.

All the while, the master had been lying well hidden in a corner of a back room, reading the same novel over and over again. It was the tale of a poor *ronin* who lived at Fuwa, in Mino Province. Finding it impossible to tide over the year end, he had in desperation stabbed his wife and his child to death and finally himself. This being a particularly pathetic story, it had a strong appeal for the master, because he saw himself in a similar plight. "Well, he had every reason for his desperate deed," he said to himself, and fell to weeping in secret.

But when at last he was informed that all the bill collectors had given up the pursuit and gone off, he recovered his composure sufficiently to emerge timidly from his place of concealment. Complaining with a sigh that he had aged several years during the ordeal of that single night, and vainly regretting his past carelessness, he went about the task of buying rice and fuel at a time when everyone else was eating *zoni* and celebrating the season.

On New Year's Day he and his family ate ordinary rice, and it was not until the morning of the second day that they could prepare *zoni* to serve to the god and the Buddha. "For some ten years," he said apologetically, "it has been our family custom to celebrate the New Year on the *second* day. Please forgive us for using such an old tray in serving you." More than that: no service was held in the evening. The year god had never dreamed that the master of this house was so poor. No sooner had the first three days of the New Year gone by, than he left the house and visited Ebisu's Shrine at Imamiya, to report to him what miserable entertainment he had received at the poor man's house, a house which so utterly belied its showy external appearance.

"It was rather stupid of you, a veteran year god, not to have known better," remarked Ebisu to him. "Before you call at a house you should investigate the financial status of the master. Never enter a house whose doorway is dirty, nor whose mat borders are frayed, nor where the mistress has to please the maid. Although Sakai is a large city, the number of poor fellows such as the one you have told me of is really only four or five at the most. It was unlucky of you to have happened to visit one of these few. I have plenty of *sake* and porgy here that merchants from all the provinces have dedicated to me; so stay and eat and drink before you return to Izumo. It will take away the aftertaste of your coarse fare." So Ebisu entertained the poor year god with food and drink and let him stay awhile with him.

The foregoing story became known to mortals only because a man who visited the shrine early in the morning of Ebisu's Day happened to hear the gods talking together in the inner sanctuary. It all goes to show that even in the society of the gods there are distinctions between rich and poor. Such being the case, how natural it is that human fortunes should be so disparate. It behooves you, therefore, to busy yourself with your regular occupation, working with all diligence, in order that the year god, who comes to you but once a year, may suffer no discomfort or inconvenience.

THE NIGHT OF INSULTS

Each locality has its own peculiar customs. In the Kanto districts there are some villages in which the festival for the god is observed on New Year's Eve. Likewise on that day, in the province of Settsu, patrons of Nishinomiya Shrine have a custom of staying at home all day long; while in the province of Buzen at Hayatomo on the same day they hold a divine service of seaweed gathering. In the secluded village of Tamba weddings are customarily held on New Year's Eve.

The mass for the dead used to be held on New Year's Eve, so that while people busied themselves with preparations for the New Year, they had at the same time to arrange incense and flowers honoring the dead. They prepared offerings on the one hand to the year god and on the other to their ancestors. To reduce the burden of their business, some wise men of those days, without serving any advance notice on Paradise, changed the mass day to July 14th. Wise men today would prefer to hold the mass during the spring or fall equinoctial season, which would prove to be an inestimable economical boon to uncounted future generations.

The festival day of the Ikutama Shrine in Osaka is set for the ninth of September. Fortunately this also happens to be the very day on which each household prepares a meal of vinegared and broiled fish. Since the celebration is the same in each household, there is no danger that guests will drop in unannounced. Just figure the savings for this one occasion alone and you will discover that it mounts up to an enormous total. In this case it appears that it was out of consideration for his patrons' purses that the god fixed this day to celebrate.

Every New Year's Eve in Kyoto at Gion, a divine service of half-shaven sticks is observed. First the sacred lights are dimmed until the faces of visitors are unrecognizable in the darkness. Next they divide the company into two groups, who then proceed to exchange insults, each side heaping as gross abuses as possible upon the other, much to the merriment of all the participants. For example:

"On one of the first three days of the New Year a rice cake will stick in your throat, and you'll be cremated at Toribeno."

"You are a partner in crime with a slave trader: both of you'll ride bareback to Awataguchi for your execution."

"On New Year's Day your wife will go crazy and throw your baby down the well."

"Messengers of Hell will carry you off in their fiery cart and eat you up."

"Your father was a town watchman."

"Your mother used to be the concubine of a Buddhist priest."

"Your sister will go out to buy bean paste without wearing her panties and tumble head over heels in the street."

Thus do they glibly fling foul words at one another, there being no limit to the catalog of abuses.

Now one of the outstanding participants in such a battle of abuse was a young man about twenty-seven or twenty-eight years old whose insults surpassed in foulness and glibness all the rest. One opponent after another went down before his filthy charges, until before long none would dare to challenge him. Just then there cut through the darkness from under a pine tree to the left a voice which called out: "Hey! big boy, you talk just like you had a new outfit of clothes for the New Year. What have you got on under that *kimono?* On a cold night like this I bet it isn't even padded!"

It was a random shot, but it struck home. The fellow was so sorely hit in a sensitive spot that he could answer not a word, but immediately lost himself in the crowd, amidst general laughter. It seems apparent from such an incident as this that nothing hurts like the truth. Anyhow, while it is still light, you'd better start making preparations for the dark of New Year's Eve, for as the proverb runs, "Poverty is a stranger to diligence."

One evening several people were walking along Sanjo Street, none too cheerfully talking together: "Where in the world has all the gold and silver gone that's flown from this flowery city?" asked one. "I wonder if the devils carried it off with them when they were chased out at bean-throwing time? It seems to me that I've been on especially bad terms with money these past few years: I haven't seen any lying about in boxes recently!"

Just as he made this last remark they saw passing by them three carts loaded with chests of money, guarded by six men, each of whom bore a lantern marked with the household crest of a chevron and three stars. Behind them walked two men who appeared to be clerks, who were talking in some such terms as the following:

"They say money's short in this world, but there's plenty of it where you find it. This consignment of money on these carts is what our old master has set aside as pocket money for his aged mother. It was first deposited in the strong room in the first year of Myoreki in the month of April, and it's making its appearance today for the first time since then: it's out for an airing after the gloom of its long imprisonment. This money reminds me of a girl who was made a nun at birth: it has never been caressed by a man nor enjoyed a good time; furthermore, it's destined to go to the temple in the end."

Splitting their sides with laughter over their own joke, the men went on talking: "Today as I was taking this money out of storage, I happened to look across into the strong room of the house annex just opposite. There were stacks and stacks of money chests with labels on them dating back to the Kan-ei era. It's a marvel how such enormous wealth could ever have been accumulated in a single generation. Generally speaking, before all else rich men of this world are misers. Anyhow, it's practically impossible to become rich without acquiring some kind of bad name. Our master, on the contrary, is in every way as generous and liberal as a born lord. Although he has lived in the lap of luxury all his life, he is still just as rich as he ever was. He seems to be the very embodiment of good fortune.

"Up until now he was content to enjoy retirement in the home of his eldest son, but now that his second son has a house of his own he has changed his mind and prefers to live with him. Since in this family the old man's will is law, beginning last November they began moving his things, and these money chests are the last load to be moved. Eleven maids were dispatched from the main house of the eldest son to wait on the old man. At the same time, seven cats moved along with him, carried in a palanquin, just like so many human beings.

"On the 21st of this month, as is his custom, the master made presents of new clothes to his employees: forty-eight suits of clothes for the men, fifty-one for the women, and twenty-seven for small and middle-sized boys and girls —a grand total of one hundred and twenty-six. They were all ordered from the Sasaya, and without exception every single employee was given an outfit. Think of what they must have cost: enough money to set a man up in business!

"As for the young master, yesterday when a theater owner came to pay his respects and in the course of conversation complained that he'd be unable to present this year's first theatrical performance for lack of funds, the master loaned him five hundred *ryo* of gold on the spot.

"Never since we entered service in this household have we at any time seen our master or his brother so much as touch money with their own hands. Of course, they have no idea how rich they actually are, for they leave all such business details to their head clerks, nine in number."

Conversing in this fashion, the two men now entered the grounds of an imposing-looking house, and after announcing that the retired master's money had arrived, they stored it in the strong room.

The year man of this household, after seeing to it that at each appropriate corner of the house a sacred candle had been lit, started to do the same for each strongroom. The master seeing it, laughed and said, "What a green year man we have here! For the owner of a mere thousand *kan* or so to burn candles at the corners of his strongroom might be quite appropriate. But if we started doing that here, we would have to light twenty-five or twenty-six candles. Does he need to light so many?"

The poor fellows who had followed along behind the procession of carts to the house were standing by envying its wealthy appearance. They continued to watch as the money chests were carried into the house one after another and stacked on the floor. The men accompanying the consignment of money, who seemed to be clerks of an exchange shop, begged the head clerk of the wealthy household to store the money away safely in one of the strong rooms. They tried their best to persuade him, pleading on their knees. But the head clerk resolutely refused to take it in, reminding them:

"Every year we have been telling you people, and by now you ought to be well aware of it, that on New

Year's Eve we will not take money in from any source after four o'clock. It's a nuisance to have to bother with such a small sum of money, and that so late at night."

After a thousand apologies, however, and extensive flattery, the messengers finally succeeded in persuading the clerk to accept it. Turning over to him the three chests of money containing the sum total of six hundred and seventy *kan,* they received the receipt for it with virtually unbounded gratitude and at last went home.

The chests of money, since the strong rooms were already shut fast, were piled up behind the cauldron in the kitchen. That's where this large fortune saw the old year out: in the kitchen, just as though it had been so much rubble or worthless stone.

THE KITCHEN FLOOR PARTIES OF NARA

THERE is something good and interesting about having the same peddler return year after year and getting to know him over a period of years. There was once a fishmonger who visited Nara over a span of some twenty-four or twenty-five years. And as he sold only octopuses he became known as "Octopus" Hachisuke. He had a goodly number of customers, which enabled him to support his family of three; yet never on a New Year's Eve had he been able to see the old year out with even so small a balance on hand as five hundred *mon*. All that he could manage on New Year's Day was to feed his family and have a bowl of *zoni*.

Since his youth "Octopus" Hachisuke had been alert to the art of getting on in life. When his widowed mother asked him to buy her a brazier he dared to take some commission from her for the service. As for the neighbors, needless to say, he would never do anything for them for nothing. Even at a time when the midwife was urgently needed, he was reluctant to fetch her until he had been treated to a hasty meal. This world is indeed filled with greed, yet that of Hachisuke was so outstanding that even when he went to buy cloth for a shroud for a deceased member of the Sutra-Chanting Club of which he himself was a member, he insisted on getting his commission on the purchase. Why, he was the sort of man who was actually glad when someone died, for then he could gouge out their eyes for his profit. Still, for all his selfishness, he remained poor; which appeared to be no more than divine justice.

It is a generally accepted fact of life that an octopus has eight legs, but from the very first day Hachisuke began peddling in Nara he made it a practice to slice off one leg and sell seven-legged octopuses. His cunning practice went unnoticed by practically everybody. Then he contracted to sell those single legs to a chophouse keeper of Matsubara, whose wont it was to buy nothing but sliced-off legs. How full of avaricious thoughts is the human mind!

Now there is a proverb which declares that "You may cheat seventy-five times, but no more," for the time is bound to come when your dishonesty will be discovered. One New Year's Eve Hachisuke cut off *two* legs from each octopus and sold six-legged ones. But still his regular customers were so busy that they did not notice the amputations. He went right on selling maimed octopuses in this fashion until he came to the middle of Tegai Street. There he was summoned to a house surrounded by a diamond-shaped bamboo fence, where they bought two octopuses. As he was leaving, the master of the house, whose head was clean-shaven like that of a Buddhist priest, glanced up from his game of *go*. Leaving off his game, he came over to Hachisuke to look more closely at the octopuses, remarking that somehow they seemed to taper off at the end. All of a sudden he thundered out, "In which one of the seven seas did you catch these anomalies? Never since the age of the gods has any book made mention of six-legged octopuses. It's a shame how you've been cheating all the people of Nara. I'll remember your face well, fishmonger!"

"Very well!" retorted Hachisuke. "And I in turn refuse to sell my octopuses to such a lazy fellow as you who plays *go* on New Year's Eve."

Later this incident was made public property, though no one seems to know exactly how it got into circulation. Since Nara was not a very large town, in every nook and corner where people gossipped the infamy of "Leg-Cutting" Hachisuke was spread, until he was no longer able to peddle there—and all because of his inordinate greed.

In Nara it is much quieter on New Year's Eve than it is in either Kyoto or Osaka. People pay for their credit purchases with all the cash they have on hand; so if they say they can't pay a bill, the collectors accept their word for it and go their way, not tarrying to press for payment. By ten o'clock in the evening, having ended their payment business, all the people of Nara set about enjoying the New Year atmosphere by holding what is called a "Kitchen Floor Party." They make a fire under the cauldron in the kitchen and spread straw matting on the earthen floor. Then, gathering from their respective rooms, the entire household, from the master on down to the lowliest maidservant, seat themselves on the matting in the kitchen. According to local custom, they take out from the baskets in which they have brought them, round-shaped rice cakes, and after broiling them eat them all together. It is a fine sight to see, and one which gives the impression that the household is quite well-off.

Low class people who live outside the town start celebrating the season by visiting first of all the home of Inaba, a retainer of the noble priest of the Daijoin Temple. After that they go around town chanting, "Wealth, wealth, wealth!" and every household hands out rice cakes and copper coins. Much the same is true in Osaka in the case of those called "evil-chasers."

When New Year's Day dawns, men sell printed pictures of Daikoku, the god of wealth, calling out, "Get your lucky fortune! Get your bales of luck!" At dawn of the second day they sell prints of Ebisu, another god of fortune, calling out meantime, "Get your Ebisu here!" And finally on the dawn of the third day it is Bishamon's pictures that they sell, crying, "Bishamon! Get your

Bishamon here!" In short, for three days they sell the gods of prosperity.

As for the rites observed on New Year's Day, the people of Nara, before making their calls upon one another, visit the Kasuga Shinto Shrine. On this occasion they invite all their kinsfolk, even to the remotest cousins, and make the occasion quite a merry one. The larger the company they gather, the greater their reputation in the eyes of the world.

No matter where you go, you will discover that it is a most enviable state to be rich. The dealers in bleached cotton of Nara sell their goods to the drapers of Kyoto on credit, collecting the money on New Year's Eve. That very same night, as soon as they have balanced their account books, they leave Kyoto for Nara with the many thousands of *kan* of silver which they have taken in for their bleached cotton, making their way by the light of a train of burning torches. The day is just dawning as the procession reaches Nara, where they store the gold and silver in strong rooms, usually finishing the balancing of their mutual debts and credits on January 5th.

In a secluded village of Yamato there once lived a group of poor *ronin* who, finding it hard to tide over the year end, thought it a good idea to plunder the procession of money chests on their way to Nara. So the gang of four plotted in secret to assault the party at the risk of their lives. The attack was successful, but when they broke open one of the chests they were dismayed to discover that it contained no petty cash such as they might use for "drink money," but only large sums, such as thirty and fifty *kan* pieces. They examined all the chests, one after another, but not daring to appropriate such large sums for drink money, in the end they abandoned them.

Then the *ronin* robbers shifted their place of operations to the Dark Pass between Osaka and Nara, to lie in wait for travellers returning from Osaka. Along came a man of small stature carrying a package wrapped in straw matting. "How very intelligent of him," they agreed, "to carry a heavy thing as though it were light. Surely he must have money hidden in it." So they attacked him, but as they made off with his package the man cried out that it would be of no immediate use to them.

When the four robbers opened the package, imagine their surprise and consternation to discover inside nothing but dried herring roe!

WHEN MASTERS EXCHANGE HOUSES

THE VERY water sounded busy on the night of December 29th as the waves of the year came washing ashore at Fushimi. The ferry for Osaka was about to leave, and since the passengers were in a greater hurry than usual they urged the boatman to cast off at once. Himself well aware that the New Year was at hand, the boatman replied, "Don't worry. I know as well as you that only two days are left in this year—today and tomorrow."

Ordinarily the passengers on the Osaka-bound ferry would not be silent. Some would be talking about public scandals, or be singing ditties, *joruri, utai,* or dance songs; while others would be amusing themselves with tall tales or imitations of popular actors. But tonight they seemed both silent and morose.

At last the ferry left the dock. The silence was broken occasionally by a muttered invocation. Or someone would vent his spleen against the world in general, complaining that in this short span of life to wait the New Year was just like waiting for one's time to come. Other passengers, unable to get their usual sleep, looked serious and worried. Then a fellow who appeared to be a petty clerk started singing loudly and long-windedly some ballads whose words he had picked up in a shady teahouse. So off-key did he hum the *samisen* accompaniment, and so grotesquely did he beat time with his head that the company was thoroughly disgusted with his performance.

Meanwhile the ferryboat had progressed as far as the Little Yodo Bridge. As it slipped between the piers stern foremost, a man who, awaking from a nap assumed a sober attitude, spoke out in a manner that seemed to indicate that he considered himself the only intelligent man aboard:

"Look here," he exclaimed, "if a man works day and night all the year round with unremitting diligence just like that water wheel over there, at the year end he will be able to balance his accounts to conform to his advance calculations. But if he is idle the rest of the year, it does no good for him to start struggling just before the end of the year."

All the other passengers, who had been listening to him, nodded their heads in approval. Among them was a man who lived on Inn Street in Hyogo. "Those words of yours went straight to my heart," he said. "Since I live near the sea I can catch plenty of fish and live comfortably. Every year, however, at the year end I discover that somehow my income has fallen just a little short of my expenditures. For the past fourteen or fifteen years now I have been accustomed to visit my maternal aunt in Otsu to ask her for some petty cash—say, seventy or eighty *momme*—anyway I've never asked her for a hundred. But this year for some reason she was so fed up with my annual requests that she turned me down flat. Since I had been taking it for granted that I could get the loan from her as easily as picking up something I'd left behind, her refusal hit me pretty hard. At present I have no idea how I'll manage to tide over the year end at home."

Another passenger spoke up: "I brought my little brother up to Kyoto to see an actor with whom I had some acquaintance. I had hoped to apprentice him to the actor's theatrical troupe and use the money that would be advanced to get safely past the year end. Though this boy is my own flesh and blood, he cuts quite a figure, so I felt sure that some day he would become a star. Sad to say, however, the actor declined to take him on as an apprentice, saying his ears were just a little too small for a regular actor. So all there was left for me to do was to bring my brother back from Kyoto.

"One thing I learned, however, and that is that there are a lot of people in this world. Every day as many as twenty or thirty boys of handsome figure and good manners and fine promise apply for admission into the troupe. In strict confidence the agents are saying that some of them are sons of *ronin* and physicians: that is, their fathers are of good blood. But since they have found it hard to tide over this year end and want to apprentice their sons to the company of actors, the manager may choose any he wants for a term of ten years at a consideration of one *kan* to thirty *momme* of silver. In point of fairness of complexion and refinement of manners boys from other districts can't hold a candle to those from the Kyoto-Osaka area. So I have to return home out of money for travel expenses."

Then another fellow spoke up and said, "My father bequeathed me a chart of the sacred names of the Buddhas which was written out by Saint Nichiren himself. Once a man in Uji wanted it so badly that he told me he would pay me any price I asked for it, but at the time I was reluctant to part with it. This year, however, being pinched for money, I went all the way to Uji to sell it to the man. In the meantime, somehow he had been converted to the Jodo sect and I found that he wasn't at all interested in the chart. As my expectations were dashed to the ground, I felt quite embarrassed. Now I have no alternative plan of procedure. In any case, it will be so annoying to return home and meet the importunate bill collectors that I intend to go straight to Mt. Koya without stopping in Osaka at all. How the omniscient Kobo Daishi must be chuckling up his sleeve!"

A fourth man now spoke up and said, "I used to sell

rice to the weavers of Kyoto on credit and see the old year out without a care in the world. The arrangement I had with them was that I supply them in December with rice on credit which cost forty-five *momme* per *koku.* At the end of March they paid me fifty-eight *momme* per *koku* for it. I ran this business every year until this one, when the clothworkers had a meeting and decided not to buy their rice from me, saying that my interest rate of thirteen *momme* per *koku* for three months was exhorbitant. They would rather celebrate the New Year without my rice, they said. So the labor I expended in shipping the rice by water as far as Toba is all lost. I've got to store it in a warehouse there and return home."

These true stories of the lives of ordinary people prove that there was no one aboard the ferry without some kind of worry or other. None of them would be able to spend New Year's Eve at home. Now, it is impossible for such men to call on friends and stay with them overnight, for unlike ordinary days, on that special day people are extremely busy. The daylight hours can be spent viewing votive tablets at shrines, but when night falls they have nowhere to go. So it is said that those who are heavily in debt usually keep mistresses in whose quarters they may hide in comfort whenever the settlement of accounts is imminent. Although such may be possible for those who have plenty of money at their disposal, it is far beyond the reach of the poor.

There was a man who from early evening began singing ditties in a leisurely manner, much to the envy of another man, who said to him, "You must already have settled all your outstanding debts." At this the singer burst out laughing and replied, "You seem to be unaware of the tactics which enable us to keep a roof over our heads, while at the same time doing each other a favor on this particular day. Several years ago we hit upon the idea of assuming each other's mastership to tide us over the year end. For example, two housemasters who are closely acquainted will exchange places for the time being. When a bill collector calls, the visiting master pretends that he is another cold-hearted bill collector and thus addresses the mistress of the house: "Madam, my bill is of a different variety from the ordinary debt. I'll settle this account with him even if I have to rip it out of his guts!" When any listening bill collector hears such ferocious language used, he gives up clamoring for the immediate payment of his bill and quits the place forthwith.

Such, in brief, is an outline of a recently devised scheme for thwarting bill collectors, which goes by the name of "housemaster exchanging." Since it is not yet widely known, it still works.

THE PILLAR RICE CAKES OF NAGASAKI

THE HAST day of November is the deadline for foreign ships to leave Nagasaki; after that day it becomes a deserted seaport. But during the period when foreign trade is allowed, the people of Nagasaki generally earn enough to live on the rest of the year. According to their degrees of fortune, rich and poor alike live comfortably, and do not have to count their pennies. As a general thing, since they buy for cash, when the customary time for the year end settlement of debts arrives, there is not much fuss. Even with the New Year approaching they go right on drinking their *sake* as usual. Indeed, in this port city life seems easier. Even in December people do not rush about, nor are any December beggars, such as we ordinarily see in the Kyoto-Osaka area, to be seen in the streets. Only by the Ise calendar are the people of Nagasaki aware of the coming of the New Year, and in conformity with time-honored custom, they make it a practice to clean their houses from top to bottom on December 13th. The bamboo rake used for sweeping up around the house is tied to the ridge of the roof and left there until the next house-cleaning day.

Each home, according to its own individual custom, makes rice cakes, the most interesting of which are called 'pillar rice cakes.' This kind of rice cake is made last of all and then stuck on the central pillar of the house (whence its name), to be eaten at the festival of Sagicho, which comes on January 15th and marks the end of the New Year celebrations.

Individual local customs, I have said, are quite interesting. In Nagasaki again, they set up in the kitchen what they call "lucky poles" in a horizontal position. On them are hung all kinds of foods: yellowtails, dried sea cucumbers, dried sea ears, wild ducks, pheasants, salted porgies, salted sardines, edible seaweed, codfish, bonitos, bundles of burdock, and other foods, all of which will be served at table during the first three days of the New Year.

After dark on New Year's Eve, beggars, their faces flushed with *sake,* visit from house to house, bearing trays on which are placed clay masks of Ebisu and Daikoku (gods of fortune), and a heap of crude salt. They call out, "The tide has come in from the sea lying in the direction from which good luck will come this year!" Does this not indeed prove that Nagasaki is the greatest port in the land?

Although it seems to be a national custom that a New Year's gift not be too expensive, the ones given out in Nagasaki are mere trifles: to men a fan, fifty of which cost one *momme;* and to women a pinch of tea leaves enfolded in a piece of paper. Since this apparent stinginess is the custom of the entire city, no one should be thought the less of for observing it.

Whatever you may say, there's no place like home. It is quite natural, then, for merchants of every province to try to settle their year-end accounts as soon as possible, in anticipation of celebrating New Year in their home towns.

In Kyoto there lived a small-scale merchant who dealt in thread and yarn. For twenty years he had made it a regular practice to visit Nagasaki annually on business. Being shrewder than anyone else, whenever he started on his journey he invariably ate a last meal at home, just before he left Kyoto, for neither on land nor on sea was he willing to spend a penny more than was necessary on anything at all. During his stay in Nagasaki he never even took a peep at the gay quarter of Maruyama. Therefore he had not the least idea how elegant Kinzan looked when seated, nor how white was Kacho's neck. At night when he retired he set an abacus close beside his pillow, and slept with an account book in his hand. He was forever figuring out how he could make a killing by cheating some gullible Chinese trader. But nowadays Chinese merchants understand and speak Japanese very well, and although they may have a lot of surplus cash on hand they won't lend it unless they have house mortgages as security. They also know that it is profitable to buy a house at a cheap price. They are now so smart that they can no longer be considered easy marks. Smarter still, however, are the native merchants of Nagasaki, who will not allow anyone to enjoy a "soft" job.

If cleverness were the only requisite for getting rich, this man from Kyoto would have been a millionaire, but he was not blessed with that *sine qua non* of riches—good luck. There were many other Kyoto thread dealers who had begun visiting Nagasaki on business about the same time as he had and who had amassed great fortunes. Thereafter they would send their clerks down to Nagasaki in their places, they themselves remaining at ease in Kyoto, beguiling the time now with sight-seeing, now with flower-viewing, and now in gay dissipation. One of them ascribed the secret of his success to what he called the "merchant spirit," which meant the constant observation of the world of affairs and trying to determine in advance what articles would rise in price the following year. Then he resolutely set about cornering that particular market, and thus by speculation made a large fortune. If one did not stake his all on the game, he would remain forever poor.

Now our thread dealer calculated very closely the difference between the purchase price in Nagasaki and the selling price in Kyoto. And his figures were never found to be very far off. However, as he was engaged in a sound business venture, he never made a killing. The margin of profit that he did realize was eaten up by the repayment of interest on loans as well as the principal. In short, though his labors were great and painstaking, it was another who reaped the profits.

Every New Year's Eve he was in the habit of putting up at an inn in Hashimoto, where he would see the old year out. It was just an old family custom, he would explain, but the truth of the matter was that he couldn't stay home because he couldn't pay his debts. If possible, he would have preferred celebrating the New Year at home in Kyoto. Ruminating on the vicissitudes of life, he came to the conclusion that on the one hand his small-scale business would probably never cause him any really serious loss; yet on the other hand, as other people rightly remarked, it would never bring him in any very large profit. "This year," he said to himself, "I must devise some plan beyond my regular business and make a large profit." Having so determined in his mind, he went down to Nagasaki, all the while cudgeling his brain to hit upon some good scheme. But after all, since only money begets money, there seemed to be no way to create it *ex nihilo*.

Wasn't there some attraction or freak of nature that he could exhibit next spring? He found it hard to think of anything, for already a variety of novelties had been created by the artisans of Kyoto and Osaka. Still, there might be just one article among the imports that would do. Anyhow, it had to be a very special kind of novelty, for anything less would be unprofitable. He considered the matter very carefully. Certain to be profitable, since none had ever been seen on any stage, was a dragon cub or a fire-eating bird. But such an anomaly was not to be obtained even in Nagasaki.

So secretly he sought out a Chinese trader and inquired

if he happened to know of any rare thing in a foreign country. "Although I have heard of them," replied the Chinese trader, "never yet have I seen a phoenix, or a thunderbird. After all, whatever is rare in Japan—such as aloeswood or ginseng—is equally rare in China." This Chinese merchant, having traversed thousands of miles of rough sea at the risk of his life, had come all the way to Japan solely in search of one rare thing—money.

Considering this to be very sensible advice indeed, the merchant from Kyoto applied himself all the more diligently to his business. But at the same time he bought various kinds of exotic birds in Nagasaki. But when he returned to Kyoto with the birds, since there were already similar ones on the market, they failed to bring him in any profit. The peacocks which he brought back, however, though already familiar to the public, were still popular. Thanks to the sale of his peacocks he was barely able to break even on the capital he had invested in the sideline business.

From this story we ought to learn this lesson: "Shoemaker, stick to your last," for after all, one's regular business is best for him.

A NIGHT AUCTION AT THE YEAR-END

NOT A year passes without people complaining that the times are bad and business is poor. But suppose you try to sell something that has a market price of ten *momme* at your own price of nine *momme* and eight *bu*. Immediately you will receive orders amounting to a thousand *kan*. On the other hand, if you offer to buy for ten *momme* something which ordinarily sells for nine *momme* and eight *bu*, you will immediately be offered two thousand *kan*'s worth. How wonderfully magnanimous are the merchants in large cities! The fact is that buying and selling depends entirely on the way people calculate.

People who maintain that what this world lacks is money must never have seen the living quarters of the rich. On the contrary, money exists abundantly in this world. This is proved by the patent fact that for the past thirty years people all over the country have been growing more and more prosperous. A house formerly thatched with straw is now shingled. The barrier house at Fuwa, described in an old poem as having the moonlight filtering in, is now roofed with tile and whitewashed. Besides, it has a strongroom and a storehouse. The sliding screens of the hall are no longer covered with gold and silver dust, for this is considered too gaudy; they are painted with gold and silver paint. Moreover, the pictures on them are drawn in India ink, elegantly enough. And so far as taste goes, it is quite the same as that of city dwellers.

Again we learn from an old poem that formerly the salt-burning women of Nada wore no combs in their hair.

But nowadays they are very particular about their *kimono* and eager to hear about and see for themselves the latest city fashions. They know that a *kimono* design of small pine trees is no longer stylish, but that the new mode is a design of bamboo in the evening sun. Also it is a fact that while suburban dwellers in even Kyoto and Osaka wear *kimono* of an outdated design of long paulownia flowers, the very latest fashions may be seen in the country. It is amusing, however, to see the word "cuckoo" dyed on the shoulder part of a *kimono* of obsolete design, or to see the red-dyed grapevines clinging to their trellises.

At any rate, wherever you may be, if you only have plenty of money, you may do as you please. On the other hand, a poor man is unable by any means to tide over the year end. If there's no money—well, there's just no money—that's all! No matter how hard a man may search the shelf, he can't find even a penny unless he previously put it there himself. Hence it is highly advisable to practice economy all the year round. If a man will save one *mon* a day, which he might spend for tobacco, in one year he will have saved three hundred and sixty-five *mon,* and in ten years three *kan* and sixty-five *momme.* If he economizes in everything—tea, fuel, bean paste, salt and the like—by such frugality he will be able to save at least thirty-six *momme* in a year, no matter how impoverished his daily life may be. When you add interest to this sum, in thirty years the total will mount up to eight *kan.* In short, one should take care every day of his life and never be negligent in even a trifle. Especially must he remember the old proverb, "At every meal with drink poverty flourishes."

There was once a poor maker of nails who barely managed to live from hand to mouth. Never a day passed but he bought eight *mon*'s worth of *sake* three times a day, having it poured into a small bottle that had once been used to offer sacred *sake* to the fox god at the time of the Inari Festival. In this manner he lived for forty-five years addicted to drink. The total quantity he consumed during these years amounted to forty *koku* and five *to,* supposing that the quantity of *sake* he drank daily was two and a half *go.* If the cost was twenty-four *mon* a day, counting twelve *momme* of silver as one *kan* of copper, over the years the sum total he spent for *sake* amounted to four *kan* and eight hundred and sixty *momme* of silver. When people made fun of this man, saying that if he were more temperate he would not be so poor, he would laugh it off, just as though he were managing his household with success. Declaring that no teetotaler had ever been known to build a storehouse, he refused to stop drinking.

One New Year's Eve, this man had practically completed his preparation for the season, with the *Horai* decorations set out, when he discovered that there was no money left to buy his usual ration of *sake.* Since for forty-five years not a day had passed but that he was in his cups, to him the thought of facing the first day of the New Year without his *sake* was unbearable. If this should occur, New Year's Day would for him be devoid of meaning. So husband and wife put their heads together, but could think of no one who might lend them the drink money; nor had they anything that they might pawn. Finally they thought of a sedge-straw hat, used the previous summer to keep off the heat of the sun, which still remained green and in good condition. Summer time would not be coming around again for quite a while. A person could sell whatever he had for his convenience, couldn't he? There seemed to be no other way to meet the immediate crisis.

So the man took the straw hat to the night auction of secondhand goods, which was by this time in full swing. All the sellers, judging by their appearance, were suffering from burdens of debt and had no one to turn to for relief. The auctioneer, spurred on by his ten percent commission, was bidding up the prices with vigor. The things he offered for sale at this year-end auction were without exception both poor and miserable. Though mute, they yet spoke eloquently of how badly their owners were in need of money.

One article being auctioned seemed to be the New Year *kimono* of a little girl of twelve or thirteen, with a seashore design dyed on a yellowish blue background. The lining was pale crimson. The *kimono* was well padded, but the sleeves had never been stitched together. When the auctioneer brought it to the hammer, the right side and the lining were knocked down for six *momme* and three and a half *bu* apiece. The lining by itself, however, was not wearable.

Next in order, half of a small yellowtail caught in the Tango Sea was brought out. It went for two *momme* and a half *bu*. After that a mosquito net made to cover a two-mat room was put up for auction. It was bid up from eight *momme* to thirty-three and a half *momme,* but in the end it was not sold, and that for a good reason. Everybody laughed, saying that the owner was to be congratulated, because instead of having had to pawn it long before, he had managed to hold on to the mosquito net until New Year's Eve.

Then there was brought to the hammer a calligraphy text written on ten sheets of specially made paper pasted together to form a long scroll, and to which was affixed the signature and seal of the author. It was bid up from one *bu* to five. The auctioneer, complaining that the bid was too low, cried out, "Why, the paper alone must be worth at least three *momme.*"

"Yes, it might be," came a voice from the crowd, "if there weren't any writing on it, but the useless calligraphy text has reduced its value to less than five *bu.*

Whoever the writer was, I say he's just a 'breechcloth artist'."

"What do you mean by a 'breechcloth artist'?" asked the auctioneer.

"Well, just as nobody lacks a breechcloth," he answered with a sneer, "nobody lacks so much skill in brush writing as this fellow!"

Next, with much care, they brought out articles labeled "fragile." There were ten china plates, between which were packed letters written by well-known courtesans of Kyoto and Osaka. Busy as the people were, they still could not resist the temptation to read them. The letters which had been written in December, they discovered, contained no mention whatever of love or passion, but were begging only for money—with appropriate and polite apologies, of course. After all, you know, love can't reach fulfillment without money.

"The owner of these fine plates," intoned the auctioneer, "must once have been called a great benefactor. Why, each one of these letters must have cost him at least one piece of silver."

"In that case," came a voice from the crowd," the old letters must be worth more than the plates are." And everybody roared with laughter.

Following that, an image of Fudo, the deity who sits amidst blazing fire, was brought forth for sale, together with a sacred club, a flower vase, a holy staff, and an old altar used for the fire-burning ritual. These were greeted with the derisive comment that Fudo was too helpless to bring about his own good fortune.

At this point the sedge-straw hat was put up for auction. Someone in the audience seeing it cried out, disregarding the fact that its owner was present, "Oh, what a shame! The owner must have expected to wear it many more summers, because it's kept in an old paper sack. What a thrifty fellow he must be!"

The first bid for the hat was three *mon,* but by the time it was knocked down at auction the bid had risen to fourteen *mon.* As the money was handed to the seller, he swore in the name of some god that he had bought it for thirty-six *mon* in May and had worn it only once: on the festival day of the blue warrior. The self-disclosure of his disgrace was truly funny to hear.

At the final auction of the night, a man bought twenty-five cases of year-end gift fans and a box of tobacco for two *momme* and seven *bu.* On returning home he opened the box. Inside, hidden under the tobacco, he found three gold *ryo* pieces—an entirely unexpected stroke of good fortune it was for him, indeed.

BLINDS FROM BRUSH HOLDERS

A CERTAIN man who had learned an unforgettable lesson from the trying experiences of the year end made up his mind that even though he had to observe the first three days of the New Year because of popular custom whether he wanted to or not, still he would start working on the fourth day. He resolved to deal strictly on a cash-and-carry basis, and would do without fish at table unless he was sure he could afford it. Moreover, during the year he would balance all his accounts faithfully on every one of the five annual settlement days. He lived thus a whole year, ever keeping in mind how exacting bill collectors are.

It was not long before another New Year rolled around. This year, he thought, he would change the dates of household events and as early as the second day he would celebrate the new day book making, which he had celebrated on the tenth day; also he would take inventory on the third day rather than the fifth as had been his custom hitherto. It was not a good idea, he thought, even to go out of the house, because if he did he might have to spend money unexpectedly, or someone might ask him to go somewhere with him, which would mean a whole precious day wasted. He spoke to others only on business, and all day and every day he occupied his time with business calculations.

"Since we live in a world where little profit is to be made," he thought, "the most important thing is to economize on household expenditures." So in March, the month when servants' contracts come up for renewal, he discharged the kitchen maid and thereafter his wife did the housework. As for himself, in the daytime he occupied his usual place as master in the shop, but after dark when the shop was closed he worked along with his apprentice boy at the mortar. Besides, he would never wash his feet with hot water but always used cold water fresh from the well, even when the weather was bitterly cold. But this man must have been haunted by the ghost of Poverty, for in spite of all his economizing his business dropped off, and he melted away like ice in the sun.

It has been well said that a one-*sho* dipper can't hold more than one *sho*. Such was the case with a certain priestess of Kumano, who used to show people pictures of Paradise and Hell and sing popular songs till her breath gave out. Despite her desperate solicitation for alms, however, she was barely able to fill her one-*sho* dipper with rice doled out in charity. The longing which people have for a happy future life exhibits itself in varying degrees, depending largely on the character of the solicitor.

One winter the priest Ryushoin went on a journey to raise contributions to restore the great image of the Buddha. He would not solicit at all from unbelievers. He just walked silently along the way, accepting purely voluntary donations. Nevertheless people donated one *kan* every step of the way, and ten *kan* every ten steps. Some even gave gold and silver. The image of the Buddha shines more brightly if it is made of metal; the solicitation of contributions goes better if the preacher looks distinguished. Be that as it may, since the present age is the high noon of Buddhism, and besides, since the restoration of the image was a special event, every Buddhist sect showed great eagerness and interest in it. Even the poor who lived on the outskirts of town donated one *mon* each, which when totaled together would be equal to the cost of a column worth twelve *kan* used in the reconstruction. After all, you ought to be careful in everything and save all the money you can, no matter how small the amount, on every possible occasion.

By the way, a man who accumulates a fortune is by nature different from other men. There was a man who sent his son to a school from his ninth to his twelfth year to learn calligraphy. During these years the boy saved all the holders of his writing brushes, as well as those used by other boys. Then in the spring that he became thirteen years old he made blinds of them and sold as many as three of them, at one and a half *momme* apiece, thus earning four and a half *momme* of silver. "This son of mine," thought the fond father, "is no ordinary person," and he said as much to the monk who had been teaching his son calligraphy. The monk, apparently not sharing the father's enthusiasm, said to him:

"During my life I have taught hundreds of boys, and not one of the smart ones like your son grew up to be a rich man, though still none turned out to be a beggar, either. They are now living at an economic level just a little below middle class. Smartness is not the only factor for success, you know. Besides, it is a mistake to think that your son is the only smart boy in the world. There are boys smarter than he is. For example, I know a boy who swept the classroom every day after practice was over, whether he was on duty that day or not. As he did so, he picked up all the sheets of paper thrown away by the other boys, smoothed them out, and sold them to a paperhanger. This was a better idea than making blinds of brush holders, for it brought in cash every day. But even that was not so good, either. Another boy I know brought extra sheets of paper along with him to his lessons, and when other boys ran out of paper, he loaned them some, charging interest of one hundred per cent a day. An enormous yearly profit for a mere boy!

All these boys had absorbed such worldly-wise methods from the lives of their profit-seeking parents. Their ideas were not the spontaneous product of their own minds.

"On the other hand, there was a boy whose parents always admonished him to devote himself exclusively to calligraphy, for they said that in the future it would stand him in good stead. Quite obedient to his parents, he devoted himself day and night to reading and writing, until in time he surpassed his seniors in brush writing. No doubt he will grow up to be a wealthy merchant, for he has learned how to concentrate on whatever task he has to do.

"After all, one can hardly succeed if he abandons the hereditary family business to start a new one. The case is the same with boys learning calligraphy: they must practice brush writing to the exclusion of everything else. To be smart in other lines is needlessly selfish; and not to be intent on matters of primary importance is a shameful thing. It cannot be truthfully said that your son is normal in mind. After all, when one is young it is best to pick flowers and fly kites, and later to settle down when he is old enough to learn the business. Now just remember what this old man of seventy has been telling you, and keep your eye on these boys to see what becomes of them in the future."

The predictions of the master of calligraphy did indeed come true. When these smart boys grew up and had to make their own living, they tried out various new ideas and failed as often as not. The one who had made blinds out of old brush holders contrived to put wooden supports on *geta* to be used in winter when the streets were muddy, but his idea enjoyed only a brief vogue. The boy who had gathered waste paper devised a method of coating pottery with pitch, but on New Year's Eve his income barely enabled him to afford one lone light. On the other hand, the boy who had devoted himself wholeheartedly to calligraphy, though seemingly slow-witted, grew to be broad-minded by nature. He invented a method to keep barrels of oil from freezing while they were being shipped to Edo by boat in mid-winter, by inserting a bit of pepper in each barrel. From this invention he realized enormous profits. The two had both been thinking of the same thing—oil. But one of them had thought in terms of earthwenware vessels, while the other thought in terms of barrels of oil.

How wide the gulf separating human minds!

HIRATARO

"WE TRUST in the Buddha to make a living," is an old proverb which still holds good.

Every year on the evening ushering in the first day of spring, the story of Hirataro is told in all the temples of the Sinshu Sect of Buddhism. Year after year the story does not vary, yet each time people hear it they are impressed anew. So usually many people, old and young, men and women, gather to listen to it.

One year the eve of the vernal equinox happened to fall on New Year's Eve. As a result, the voices of the bill collectors were mingled with the incantations of the men casting out devils, while the clink of money balances blended with the sound of bean throwing. This rather weird atmosphere reminded one of the expression, "A demon in the dark." At a Shinshu temple in Osaka the priest beat a drum, offered the sacred tapers before the altar, and awaited the arrival of worshipers. Yet even after the midnight bell had tolled, and the priest had gone through all the rituals, only three visitors were to be seen in the hall. The priest being forced to acknowledge that the world was utterly worldly, addressed the worshipers in these words:

"Because tonight happens to be the deadline for the settlement of all debts of the old year, worldly people seem to be too busy to attend the services. I should think, however, that even tonight any grandmother who has retired from active household management would have nothing to do. When that boat arrives from the other world to ferry her across the river, she cannot refuse to board it. How foolish people are! What a pity, what a shame to neglect the services of the Buddha! But now it seems of little use to preach a sermon to only three people. Although these are spiritual services to the Buddha, a few material considerations must also be taken into account. Since the offerings of you three will scarcely pay for the candles burned, it seems uneconomical to preach. Would you kindly take back your offerings and go home? To have come here at a time when people are so absorbed in their worldly affairs is none the less praiseworthy on your part. You may rest assured that the Buddha will see to it that your attendance tonight will not have been in vain. He will have it recorded in his golden ledger to balance your accounts in the future life. So I beg you not to think that your piety tonight has done you no good at all, for the Buddha is all charity. This I speak in earnest. You may depend upon it absolutely."

An old woman who had been listening began to shed tears and said, "Your inspiring words have made me thoroughly ashamed of myself. I must confess that I did not come here from any pious motive. My only son has been neglecting his business, and every year end until now he has managed to get by with some excuse or other, but this year he was unable to think of any. At last he asked me to come here, so that after I was gone he could make a racket, crying out that his old mother was missing. Then while the neighbors beat drums and gongs all night long, he could go around pretending to be searching for me. Such was his scheme for tiding over the year end. He boasted that it was an original idea he had just thought up in order to outwit the year-end bill collectors by crying, 'Come back! Come back, Grandma!' It is unfortunate for me that I have a son who is so good-for-nothing, but what a pity it is that I should sin unwillingly by giving my neighbors so much trouble!"

Another person, a man from the province of Ise, spoke up: "Fate is forever a mystery," he said. "At first I was quite a stranger in this big city for I had no relatives here. But since I was employed by a clerk of the Grand Shrine of Ise responsible for the subscribers living in the Osaka district, I would visit this city carrying on my back things to be delivered to them. Seeing what a prosperous city Osaka was, I thought that a family of two or three might easily make a living here doing something or other. Fortunately I made the acquaintance of a widow of a haberdasher who used to peddle his wares in Yamato Province. She was a plump, fair-skinned woman, with a two-year-old son. I married her, thinking that with both of us working we might live comfortably, and that when I grew old I could depend upon the boy to provide for me.

"But in less than a year after our marriage I lost what little money we had due to my lack of experience in peddling, and from the first of December I have had to think seriously of finding another job. Meantime my wife, neglecting me entirely, doted on her son exclusively, often saying to him, 'Listen to me carefully, for you have ears. You must know that although your dead papa was a small man he was clever. He even cooked, which is a woman's task. He would let me go to bed early, while he sat up until dawn making straw sandals. He wouldn't buy himself a *kimono,* but he had new ones made for you and me to wear in the New Year season. This bluish-yellow one here brings back fond memories of him. In fact, everything reminds me of that dear old man. Son, you do well to cry for your papa who is gone forever.'

"Hearing her talk like this vexed me because of my position as the spouse of an heiress, but all I could do was to put up with it. I had a little money due me from some people in my native province; so thinking that I might be able to tide over this year end by collecting it, I went all the way back to Ise. Quite unexpectedly, however, I found that my debtors had all left for parts unknown. So I returned this evening just before supper, without any money in my pockets.

"When I entered the house I found rice cakes and firewood. Moreover, the table to be dedicated to the New Year god had been properly decorated with ferns. There must still be some hope left, I thought, for the world was as kind as it was cruel. However that may be, I had my wife's good husbandry to thank for all these things prepared in my absence. I felt pleased, and when my wife saw that I had returned, she seemed more affable than usual. First she brought me water to wash my feet with, and then set before me a supper of sardines, some vinegared and some broiled. Just as I started to eat them, she asked me if I had brought the money from Ise. No sooner did she learn of my failure than she began bawling me out:

" 'How dare you come back empty-handed! The rice you are eating was obtained by mortgaging my very person. Unless I pay ninety-five *momme* by the end of February I shall be lost. Other people's rice costs only forty *momme,* while ours costs us ninety-five *momme* solely because you are good-for-nothing. You came to this house with no dowry but your breechcloth, so you'll lose nothing by clearing out right now. It will be dark tonight, so you'd better leave before it's too late."

"So saying, she took away the dishes from before me and urged me to be on my way. Meantime neighbors had come thronging in, and siding with my wife, they said, 'It must be embarrassing to you, but your position as spouse of the mistress is a weak one. If you are a man at all, you'd better leave this place and try your luck somewhere else.' At the time I was too sad even to cry.

Tomorrow I shall return to my home province, but I was so completely at a loss as to where to spend tonight that I came here, even though my denomination is Nichiren."

When his story, at once funny and pitiful, was finished, the last of the three temple visitors laughed aloud and said, "Now it's my turn to tell my story, but please excuse me from telling you who and what I am. I can't stay at home without being tormented by bill collectors, and nobody will lend me even one red cent. I felt chilly and wanted a drink, so I hatched up first one scheme and then another, but in the end could think of none that would tide me over the year end. At last I concocted a shameful plan: tonight the story of Hirataro would be told at the temple and crowds of people would come to hear it. While they were listening I would steal their *geta* to get drink money. Contrary to my expectations, however, very few people are to be seen tonight in any temple, and so the job that was to be done under the very eyes of the Buddha is just impossible."

The man shed tears as he told his story. The priest was deeply moved and said, "Well, well! Though all of you are endowed with the body and mind of the Buddha, it appears that your poverty begets all manner of evil schemes. But such is the sad way of the world."

As with a sigh he was deploring the world of men, in rushed a woman to inform him that his niece had just given birth in an easy delivery. On her heels came a man with a message that the funeral of Kuzo the box-maker, who had hanged himself after a quarrel with a bill collector, would be held after midnight. The priest was cordially invited to come out to the burial ground. In the midst of the ado caused by this good news and bad news, a tailor entered to report that the white padded silk *kimono* which the priest had asked him to make had been stolen by a thief. The tailor promised that if after a search he was unable to recover it, he would reimburse the priest to spare him any possible loss.

Then a man who lived just east of the temple came in to ask the priest to allow him to draw water from the temple well during the first five days of the New Year, because his own well had run dry. After him came the only son of an influential parishioner who, because of his dissipation, had been disinherited by his father. Finding it absolutely necessary for him to leave his father's house at once and go elsewhere, his fond mother had thought of placing him under the care of the priest until the fourth day of January. Such a request as this from so rich a parishioner no priest could deny.

So we see that the "priest in December," so long as he lives in the world of men, is far from being free from involvement in human affairs.

THE PERENNIALLY PROSPEROUS SHOPS OF EDO

In the streets of Edo peace reigns abroad, and people from all over the land are eager to do business there. Shops of every variety are open for business, and never a day passes but goods from every province in the country are shipped in by boat and packed in on the backs of thousands of horses. No further proof is needed that there is an abundance of gold and silver in the world, and it would be a pity indeed if a merchant were unable to lay hands on at least a bit of it.

From December 15th onward Tori Street, with its prosperous establishments, looks exactly like a treasure mart. Ordinary things for daily use are pushed aside in favor of goods displayed only at the New Year's season: battledores and shuttlecocks, mallets of good fortune inlaid with silver and gold, and similar luxuries. Even a miniature bow sells for two *ryo* of gold, for in Edo not only the lords but also the townspeople are extremely openhanded.

Along every street the stalls that are set up are doing a brisk business. Copper coins flow like currents of water, while silver piles up like drifting snow. Visible in the distance is Mt. Fuji, rising in all its magnificence against the horizon, while the footsteps of people streaming across Nihon Bridge sound exactly like the passage of thousands of wagons along the highway. Every morning fish are sold in such quantities in the Funa Street market that one may well wonder whether or not the supply in the seas surrounding our fair islands has been exhausted.

Every day to the vegetable market of Suda Street in Kanda are brought such quantities of radishes by thousands of pack horses that it seems as though the very radish fields themselves were moving into town. So high are the heaps of red peppers in baskets that although we are in the province of Musashi, we can well imagine ourselves to be gazing down from the top of Mt. Tatsuta in all its autumnal glory. The wild ducks for sale in Earthenware and Malt Streets appear like black clouds descended to earth. All along Hon-machi Street the drapers display particolored cloth of scattered designs, whose patterns originated alike with warriors' wives and ladies' maids. Some depict scenes in springtime, others those in summer, and still others those in autumn and winter. One can enjoy the sights of all the four seasons there at once. Again, in the dry-goods shops of Temma Street the cotton goods remind one of the snow on Yoshino at dawn. When evening comes, lanterns are hung up in shop fronts, casting their light out into the street. New Year's Eve, the time when merchants make their largest transactions in a single evening, is worth a thousand *ryo* of gold.

As for *tabi* and *geta,* the artisans of Edo habitually wait to purchase them last of all, just before the New Year begins to dawn. But one year it happened that not even a single sock or a solitary shoe was to be found for sale in all of Edo. As might have been anticipated, in the greatest city of Japan the demand was for thousands of pairs. Whereas in the early evening the price of a pair of *geta* was only seven or eight *bu,* after midnight it rose to one *momme* and two or three *bu,* and by dawn it had soared to two and a half *momme.* Even at this price, although there would have been buyers, there were no sellers.

Another year, a couple of small porgies were priced at eighteen *momme;* still another year, a single decorative orange cost two *bu.* Despite such fancy prices people of Edo did not refrain from buying them. In Kyoto and Osaka, on the contrary, people won't buy things even by chance if the price is exhorbitant. It has well been said of Edoites that they are lordly-minded. When narrow-minded people who have lived a long time in Kyoto or Osaka move to Edo, they find themselves so adapting to the spirit of Edo that in time they do not even count their coppers or verify the exact weight of their gold coins. If by mischance a coin of short weight is taken in, it is merely passed along to the next fellow with no further ado. Since money is forever changing hands anyhow, why make a fuss about it?

On about the 17th or 18th of December in the shops of the money carriers can be seen heaps of silver and gold, shining bright as ever. No one can tell how many times a year that money will be travelling between Edo and Kyoto or Osaka. There's nothing in the world that works like money. Yet even with all this money, there are still people who have to face the coming of the New Year without a single gold coin in hand—even in Edo.

As regards New Year's presents, the usual ones are swords (not real ones), *kimono, sake,* fish, or boxes of candles. Each of them gives promise of a spring that will last forever. Even the gate pines before each home symbolize the first stage in the ascent of that Mount of Everlasting Prosperity. And so, as over the Evergreen Bridge the New Year dawns in a calm and cloudless sky, the sun sheds its beneficent beams over all.